Thirty-Five
and Counting

Thirty-Five and Counting

James C. Schaap

Illustrations by Norman Matheis

Dordt College Press
Sioux Center, Iowa

Published by Dordt College Press
Sioux Center, IA 51250
Copyright © 1985 by Dordt College Press
All rights reserved
Printed and bound in the United States of America

ISBN 0-932914-11-X

Contents

I. Essays

II. Stories

ACKNOWLEDGMENTS

Grateful acknowledgment is made to the following magazines and newspapers, who first printed the pieces specified, somtimes under different titles and in slightly different form.

The Banner: "Comfortable, Familiar, and Ever So Deadly," "Electric Socks and the Incarnation," "Ghost Towns," "Homecoming," "Home for Christmas," "The Last of the Frisians," "Marking Time," "Real Estate," "Special Music," "Thanksgiving," "Thirty-Five and Counting," and "To Do, Or Not To Be."

Calvinist Contact: "The Immigrant" and "Prophet With A Cane."

Campus Life: "Poodles Corner" and "Revival Fires."

The Chicago Tribune: "We, the Vietnam Spectators."

Christian Educators' Journal: "On Learning, and Teaching, Identity," and "Right and Wrong."

Christian Home and School: "Education and Eccentricity," "Learning by Heart," "On Winning, and Losing," and "The Testimony of History."

The Church Herald: "Andy," "Bean-Walking," "Bingo," "Breaking Away," "Canonization for Anna," "Death of a Dominie," "Kidney Stone," "Leap-Frogging," "Prairie Story Revisited," "Prayer and Lake Perch," "Seagulls and Sovereignty," Small Town Sin," and "Winter Thaw."

The Madison (WI) Capital-Times: "Babylon: Or Coming of Age at the State Tournament."

The Milwaukee Journal: "Sounds of Shattered Silence" and "Walking Billboards."

The Reformed Journal: "Factory Second" and "Mason Tender."

For Calvin and Jean Dirkse Schaap

O God, Thou has taught me from my youth;
And I still declare Thy wondrous deeds.

And even when I am old and gray,
O God, do not forsake me,
Until I declare Thy strength to this generation,
Thy power to all who are to come.

Psalm 71:17, 18

Prayer and Lake Perch

I love lake perch, and so do my parents. When I was a boy my family would (very infrequently) venture out to a lakeshore tavern for deep-fried lake perch. Somehow, fresh lake perch tasted great in a tavern, even though the Calvinist culture in which I was reared hinted that something originally sinful breathed and grew in that dimly lit world.

But my parents would chance the moody darkness and the seductive icy tinkling of mixed drinks just for a bite of lake perch, with an order of cole slaw in a stout paper cup. Together we'd sit there and pray while the girl in the black stockings waited with a dish full of tartar sauce. In the world, I suppose, but not of it.

And it seemed to me then, a ten-year-old covenant child, ill-at-ease in the foggy and dark city of man, that my bowed head made me even more conspicuous than I already was, even more of an outsider in an elbows-up world of friendly conversation. Just being in a bar was enough of a shock when I was a boy. Praying so noticeably seemed akin to lugging a cross through the swinging doors and hoisting it up on our table, an unnecessary demonstration of something we didn't really have to bring up in the first place. Even without a bowed head I felt purple in a bar.

A few years later at fifteen, the stool sitters seemed to me a more compelling group than they once had appeared—happy, affable, relaxed, some of them leaning up against the bar's thick black padding while holding their tap beers in one hand, all the while laughing and enjoying themselves.

And there our family would sit, praying over our perch, looking like some Amish awkwardly strolling through a shopping center. At fifteen it wasn't simply awkward for me to pray in public, it was embarrassing. But then, at fifteen, one's whole family is something of an embarrassment, I suppose.

At twenty, I was sure everything my parents did was not only embarrassing, but also plain wrong. So I'd smile at the bar girl when she stood there waiting for my father's head to come up, a fancy Pabst tray full of drinks in her hand and a bottle of ketchup for our fries in the other. I'd smile as if I knew exactly what she was thinking. Confident of the breadth of my learning, at twenty I was confident such public prayer rose, at most, to the haze of cigarette smoke at the ceiling—only that far.

Such silly piety, I would have said then, flows from either of two purposes, neither of which is sincere motivation. Maybe it's custom: my father has prayed through years of meals, and the habit is so thoroughly fixed within him that he cannot eat without satisfying the urge for ritual. But custom alone is not motivation enough for prayer, I would have argued. Worse, maybe it's a desire to witness: the outside chance that one of the men bellied up to the bar will note my father's bowed head and start mending his ways that very evening. But talking to God so others can see you smacks of the hypocrites in Matthew 6: "They love to stand and pray in the synagogues and at street corners, that they may be seen by men." Wrong, wrong, wrong, I would have said, at twenty.

But I'm older now, and today I think I know even more. For instance, I think I know that my parents were wrong, in a way, for making me bow my head in a dimly lit tavern. As long as, for me, such prayer was awkward or embarrassing or out-of-place, such a practice was mere exhibitionism. It wasn't prayer at all. And what I whispered during those suppers reflected the banality of the exercise: I would chug through a sort of ritual litany of blesses, a childhood memory prayer that included my grandparents

—"bless - mamma - and - daddy - and - Judy - and - Gail -and - Grandpa - and - Grandma -" —years after both of them had passed on to a place where they had no need of further blessing. Put your head down, quickly get out the words, jerk your head up again—then watch your mother smile. It wasn't prayer, really.

I think I know it was a little bit wrong, because today I think I know more about prayer. I know that those ditties I rifled through over a plate of perch were not really prayers; I wasn't really speaking to God—I was fulfilling an obligation to my parents. Prayer is, of course, nothing more or less than talking with God, and one cannot really sacramentalize prayer with folded hands and bowed heads, as if the occasion were some formal affair of Sunday-best.

I grew up singing "Prayer is the soul's sincere desire, / unuttered or expressed, / the motion of a hidden fire / that trembles in the breast." Singing that, I learned that prayer was a spontaneous offering, the fluid, natural communication which flows from creature to Creator. Prayer is not a pose; it's a function—"the Christian's vital breath," the song says.

And today, I'm old enough to learn from no less a heretic than D.H. Lawrence that such natural communication between God and man exists only in a heart attuned to God. Belief, he says (and so have many others), comes only from the Holy Ghost within. So while such public prayers may well have been natural for my parents, they were not for me—not at ten, or fifteen, or twenty.

All of that I think is true. But today I forgive my parents because I know that, in a way, all of that coercion was right—odd as that seems to be. Today my own children are coming to that age when they look at me across the table and wonder whether their father will pray in such an odd place to eat supper. And the problem is, there's more to worry about when you're a father. All this knowledge one accumulates chasing through life's experiences gets to be a burden at times. While I'm convinced that forcing them, as I was forced, to bow their heads in public will not ensure that real prayer takes place, I am committed to

15

doing whatever I can to ensure that their sweet kid's hearts become attuned to God. I want the Holy Ghost to dwell in those darling little temples. And I know—as I am sure my parents knew—that the only way God may come to dwell within them is if they ask Him. And I know—as I am sure my parents knew—that one asks Him to dwell within, only through prayer.

I wonder sometimes how God receives all our prayers, even those shot-from-the-hip—the prayers mustered up as much from a sense of duty as from a real heartfelt desire. I can't help but think they're recorded anyway—even if no sweat or blood certifies the efforts. He is, after all, our Father, and if anyone will understand our silly foibles, surely He will, our great grace-giver. We have, I know, His promise to listen, even when our efforts are soiled by conditioning or coercion.

Sincere desire prompted my father's bowed-head testimony; it was a sincere desire that all of us remember, especially in a bar, whose children we really were. I'm sure God smiles on that kind of devotion.

So I suppose today I too should look over the table with that same furrowed-brow look my father gave me when I was a boy, and use it to convince my children to bow their heads. And silently we'll pray, sitting there rather uncomfortably. And then we'll eat lake perch. I love lake perch.

Today half the county comes out to their favorite tavern for fish dinner on Friday nights. Years ago, the perch were taken right from the big lake down the road; some fish-lovers ate perch on Fridays to support local industry. Years ago, the county's Roman Catholics had to eat fish on Fridays; some fish-lovers ate perch to fulfill ecclesiastical law. But today, the perch are Canadian, probably flown in; years ago already the Pope freed Roman Catholics from a special Friday diet.

So today there are only two good reasons why all these folks wait in a line along the bar for fried lake perch on Friday nights: custom (they've been doing it for years) and pure desire (they love perch). And really, those two reasons are inseparable; they love perch—at least partially—because they've loved it for years.

In that way, Friday night perch is like prayer, I guess. Prayer—real prayer—is a natural function of a heart attuned to God. But atonement comes only by prayer, and one learns to pray by praying. Thus custom builds desire. Thus desire builds custom.

That's what my father thought, I suppose. And that's why I'll carry on that tradition, even into the tavern.

Andy

Last week my mother called just to say that things were fine and so forth. No real news, it's just that calling seems to be so much easier than sitting down and writing and all. And if you do it at the right time it really doesn't cost all that much either. So my nephew cut his foot at school and my niece is growing nicely, almost talking already, and my sister's oldest is enjoying school. And, oh yes, do you remember Andy? I think he was a year older than you were. Well, he's not well at all now. And it's been really rough on him and his parents. Maybe his death will be some kind of release, you know? The whole story is so sad. You remember him, don't you? You haven't been away that long.

Yes Mom, I remember Andy. I remember him as a long dangling vine of a boy who wasn't the worst of the fifth grade basketball players. And I remember that he played third base on the little league baseball team, although he didn't play all that much, just some warm-ups and maybe late in the game if we'd be way ahead or way behind. And I remember him as being smart, too. Never the first one down in a spelling-bee; maybe not the smartest in the class, but no clown. But more than all that, I remember him defending himself against most of the others, myself included, fighting for something which I can only today identify as dignity. Andy was willing to swing, willing to suffer split lips for something money couldn't buy, and something he probably never felt he achieved. Andy was different.

He lacked nothing upstairs, and he was never the last kid chosen in playground basketball, but we all knew that at any moment, anywhere, he could fall over as if he had been shot by some invisible assassin. Right in the middle of a game, four on four, suddenly we'd discover him, legs and arms akimbo, sprawled out over the cold, wet blacktop, his body quivering and jumping and rolling as if something or someone in him was trying frantically to break free. His eyes still roll in my memory, and I see that contorted face so clearly that if I were an artist I could easily draw it, always bent off to the left shoulder at the neck, jerking, snapping, as if trying to pull itself away from an image it saw in a mirror.

Andy fell into these spells frequently. By the time we were in the third grade, we were quite used to it, really. Oh, it was disconcerting to teachers, but we all knew what to do, and if some young first-year teacher from Michigan didn't, any one of us would explain in no time. It could happen right in the middle of singing; we stood: "Hallelu-hallelu-hallelu-hallelujah!!," and the girls stood: "Praise Ye the Lord!" Up we'd come again: "Hallelu-hallelu-halle..."; and there he'd be, spilled off his desk, legs split, jerking in the aisle, his arms snapping and twitching.

Even in high school. Typing class. Even in band where he was not a bad trumpeter. Again, at noon in the gym, all the girls watching as they sat around on the bleachers and whispered.

I guess that's what made him so irritable. We never really teased him about it—not even kids could be so crass—but it was there and we knew it. So when we'd get in little arguments about who touched the ball before it went out of bounds, Andy would erupt into violent anger. Someone would tease him about talking to some ugly school girl and he'd come out swinging, those long arms reaching and punching as if they could destroy all of us and this frothing devil within him with little more than his own power.

Then, when he was about sixteen, it was over. He never fought. He never had any more attacks. He rarely even came in the restaurant anymore. He never talked to us. He only went to school. His eyelids barely moved all day. He walked slowly. He stumbled down steps in the old brick, three story high school. His head dropped down, his neck loose, he seemed always to be nearly sleeping. And it was safe for us. Rarely did he explode into a frantic rage. Rarely did we find him sprawling on the floor in some contorted and horrifying fit. And it was all so safe. The answer was dope. No, he never bought it off the street; he never had to. It came from the doctor, and it changed his life. He stopped playing in the band. I don't even remember him as a senior.

And then I left to go to college. Occasionally my mother would speak of him when I visited. "Andy's in Memorial Hospital," she'd say. "Mental ward." Several years later: "Andy's at the County Hospital; you know they don't put them there unless they don't think they'll come back." Sometime later: "Andy's at Pine Rest—Ben Vander Aa was in Grand Rapids and he thought he'd try to talk to him. Said he was really bad, couldn't even understand a word."

So Andy's not been in my mind for many years. And Andy's not had his own mind either for many years. Our Andys are so pleasant to forget, because our Andys are an inconvenience in our lives and even make us miserable. They disturb our order. They sprawl out in our beautiful suburban lives like horrid nightmares, like very unwanted guests. Our Andys are dried blood on a clean white shirt. And when they die we say that we remember them, because a memory is sometimes a rather safe place for us to hide.

And it's easy to come up with some Pharisaical way of dealing with our Andys and their slow but often inevitable ends. "There but for the grace of God. . ." is a favorite. "Andys teach us to be thankful for what we are." "Andys humble us." "Andys are God-given symbols of our own sin and misery."

But Andy wasn't a symbol; he wasn't an object for my pride. Andy was a human being. He looked like all the rest when he put on his suit for swimming lessons. And often I saw him cry. I heard him laugh. I heard him swear. I heard him pray when it was his turn. I saw blood squirt from his lips. And he was always so embarrassed after a seizure, and angry because he never really knew it had happened himself. It was something outside of him, something that possessed him— something that finally killed the spirit in him.

Sometimes easy answers aren't sufficient. Sometimes we can't dismiss our Andys with some kind of cheap theology. Sometimes it's wrong to see our Andys in a kind of concentric world where everybody else exists only to teach us some truth. That kind of world is built on something called pride.

I don't know what to do with Andy today. I don't know where he fits in my neat little catechism; I don't know if it's even right for me to think that I'm supposed to learn something from Andy's life. Maybe it's good for us to be awed by the sheer complexity of this world God has created, the world we have messed.

Sometimes there's little we can do but work and pray.

Education and Eccentricity

Going home for the holidays has its small benefits as well as its big ones, for in addition to all the sugar-frosted cookies, the fudge and fruit cake, and the occasionally delightful family gossip, one gets to refresh one's memory with the nearly forgotten images of childhood. I take out my car and drive as slowly as my grandmother used to, following the winding river where my friends and I used to trap muskrats, or, further east, skirting the lakeshore woods, we used to haunt; and I look for stocking caps and woolen mittens on kids hoping to find arrowheads or rifle shells or other treasures of childhood—just as I once did.

And I drive past old houses which I thought had completely passed from my memory, living away from my hometown as I have been. The land, the houses, the barns—all conjure very real characters from the old days. They jump into my memory from bushes or barns or bridges, an amusingly eccentric cast of personalities as precious to me as the Canterbury pilgrims were to Chaucer.

Just west of the river there's a field today grown a quarter acre larger than it was twenty years ago, now that the house is gone. George Aderman lived there in an old homestead shack, its dilapidated porch leaning away from the house and toward the road. Today the old house is gone; some farmer is harvesting sweet peas where George used to cook his oatmeal. And George is gone. But he is still very much alive in my memory. I see him yet, his silver hair as scrambled as a broken bale of hay atop his pointed head. I see him holding the red hymnal so close to his eyes you would think the book was some precious document, which it probably was in its own way. He'd never sing along, but he'd work at reading the words. I remember my grandpa explaining how he had offered to buy Aderman a pair of glasses, but old George told grandpa not to bother—"I really don't need them that bad," he said. George died without heirs.

Then there is Mrs. Kloosdyk, an old widow with two bad legs and something of a beard, who was, lest anyone should dare to forget, of the upper class in the old country. It was a peculiar old-world memory; for many years she lived below another widow, one floor up, but they never talked—Mrs. Kloosdyk was conscious, after all, of who she was. On Sunday they both went to the same church, but in different cars.

We were all scared to death of Anna Kloosdyk, and if the truth be known, there were a few moms in our little church who threatened their wiggly boys with our fear of the woman. "Sit still," they'd whisper, "or we'll make you sit next to Mrs. Kloosdyk." It was sure cure.

And I remember Sam Freiling, the man who walked the streets of the village daily with his wide wheelbarrow in front of him, his ax lying within like some threat. Out to the woods south of town he'd go every morning, returning at noon, the steel-gray wheelbarrow full of split wood. His shoulders slouched, we thought, from his split wood calling. Whose wouldn't, we'd say, pushing that wheelbarrow every day like he did. We watched him buy black bananas and day-old bread from the grocer's back room, and we'd scrunch up our noses. Sam Freiling, like Mrs. Kloosdyk and George Aderman, is gone now, of course.

There was Elmer Bergman, too. He used to live just outside of town, walking distance. Elmer thought he could sing, so he started taking lessons from the spinster voice teacher when he was nearly sixty years old. And Alma Semphill—we were sure her old Chevy never got out of second gear. She used to live in that little brick place—you remember?

And there are more. Driving through the old haunts is

24

like paging through an album you forget you had. So I'm thinking about all these eccentrics one night—why is it there are no more interesting characters like the ones there once were, the kind we thought so peculiar, so fascinating as children?

One reason, I assume, is that my perspective has changed. Child-like enchantment has matured into mid-life cynicism, perhaps. Besides, professors of English are not in position to keep company with the likes of Bergman and Freiling. Maybe they are there, but I don't see them.

But more than perspective has changed. Few of the lovely eccentrics of my youth ever had the blessings of mass education. Strange as that may seem, at least part of their uniqueness is attributable to a lack of formal learning. Although it may be sad to have to admit it, mass education does wash us of our peculiarities. It sets us in lines and then shoves us out, one after another, into the world. The most backward of home environments must change if the children of that home spend eight or more hours per day, nine or ten months per year, with an educated teacher and twenty or thirty peers. For better or worse, it happens.

If in fact there is a lack of colorful characters today, and if in fact education is at least partially responsible for their extinction, then the phenomenon is worth examining for just a minute. If mass education has made us remarkably similar, then mass education is remarkably powerful, more powerful than most of us may have guessed. School is more than a system of educated babysitters waiting in a series of brick rooms, marked Grade 1 to Grade 12, and it isn't just a place where our kids go to learn how to fix a transmission, or run a hardware store, or preach a sermon, or heal the sick, or build a house. School molds people, changes them into the kinds of characters the society desires its children to become.

Our schools reflect those attributes we want in an individual; we upholster our curriculums with those attitudes, beliefs, concerns, even the career goals we deem best for our children.

So just exactly what kind of people does this society

desire? Into what molds are our kids being cast? Those questions become the real questions about education and schools. And the people who see that kind of question clearly, the people who know that school is a determining factor in shaping the life of an individual, the people who know that school changes us, those people—if they are Christians—have absolutely no choice in systems. Their belief demands that their school be a Christian school.

It's a strange lesson to learn from Aderman and Freiling and all the rest of the eccentrics, but it seems to me to make sense.

Anna

Anna is out of intensive care now, and I guess that's why I'm saying this. Because it strikes me—now that she has wrestled through a fight with her heart—it strikes me that we are far too good at eulogies. Nice things are always easy to say after the funeral. But today Anna came out of intensive care.

Anna is an organist in our church—self-taught for the most part—and a Sunday school teacher for three or four generations probably. When I was a boy we feared Anna because her grim face wore no emotion; her lips were locked together in a twist that was neither smile nor frown. We read it as perpetual disgust.

Sunday school programs brought out the worst in her. A hundred kids with lit fuses would shoot around the church sanctuary during practice the night before. "You fourth graders, act your age!" She would always snap at us. We were sure she had no loving voice in her. When she'd turn to the fifth graders, someone would mimic her for sure. Years later I discovered that Anna created those annual programs.

Anna never married. In a church of families, even kids don't quite know how to take women who don't marry. They're different, and a boy starts recognizing such things about the same time he starts reading the script writing carved into the Communion table at the front of the church he's attended for ten years. Suddenly, it's just there. Fourth-grade boys just figured a woman like Anna—sour Anna—couldn't get a man. Meanwhile, another Christmas program would come and go.

Halfway through adolescent rebellion, I thought Anna was an icon of the staid, traditional, immovable church of my youth. Fashions arrived and left, but Anna's hair looked forever the same, as if she'd surrendered to being out of time. I swore that the older she grew the slower she played the organ, until even the bouncy hymns poked along like the old psalms. And always you'd see the expressionless face up there, lighted by the soft glow of organ light. She chewed gum, not vigorously but quickly, nervously, when she played.

Years have passed since then. Today the church pays a music director to order a Christmas show from some slick Christian catalog out of Texas, but Anna is still teaching Sunday school, and now she has my own three-year-old boy. No one else her age teaches, because kids have a way of forcing early retirements, just as they always did. But there is a smile on Anna's face whenever we drop our son off with her for Sunday school. It's a smile unlike anything we ever saw before on her face, a smile that surprised me at first. And Anna has a permanent now, her curly gray hair curled up tight around her head like any of a dozen other women in church.

Time fills in gaps the way dawn colors a lakeshore landscape. Some things I know now about Anna. I know now that Anna cared for her parents until the day each of them died. I know now that her father was no gentle man to live with—blustery, hardheaded, stubborn as the toughest Hollander. I know now that when he was gone, every Sunday she dressed her mother, set her in the wheelchair, and pushed the old woman to church, even when she knew her mother understood little of the sermon. I know now that giving her life to them was a thankless, blessed job that might have turned anyone's face into something grim, something less than radiant.

I know now that the woman who never married regularly plays grandmother to two little blond-haired boys no older than my own son, two little boys her niece was left alone with when their father ran off with another woman.

28

Why does she smile that way today, twenty years after a class of fourth-grade boys decided she was much too owly to be a good teacher? Why does my son love her today? Why does he curl around my leg and turn away from her when she talks to him, as if he's embarrassed to have all of her attention himself? Why does Anna smile?

Maybe it's because life is easier for her now, later on in her years. Maybe the privileged burden of her parents' care is there behind her, settled in the pages of her mind like yellowed photographs. Maybe the anxiety of being alone has settled into a firm assurance that all things have worked together for good. Maybe playing grandmother has swelled the limits of her tolerance. Maybe the smile is simply the inherent reward of many years of Christmas programs interspersed annually in a lifetime of quiet selflessness.

Four hundred years ago we reformed the church and stopped canonization, stopped making saints. Maybe it's a shame. Today we don't know how to revere those who give themselves, all of themselves, through us to God. We let them pass on too easily, and we don't elevate them like heroes. After all, what was Abraham to David but a symbol of belief and courage, of faith and promise.

So this is for you, Anna. And this is for me. And this is for our son. And this is for our Lord.

I'm happy you're out of intensive care, and so is my son.

Home for Christmas

Most children are shamelessly selfish at Christmas, and what's worse, little can be done about it. "What are you going to get me for Christmas?" our kids ask, about the same day the phony Christmas trees, perfectly blue-green, sprout from behind the counters of most every store in the mall.

So we dust off the old sermon on "the Greatest of Gifts," and subtly create some pointed homily on the blessedness of giving. But it doesn't work. So, like Scrooge himself might, we threaten to call off the whole tinseled affair this December. But the kids know it's a bluff; they know full well that Christmas is their holiday. They know it when they see us loiter in the toy department, ponderously wandering in and out of the triple-stacked rows, trying to guess which gadgets might make it through January. They know, the little stinkers, that we give because we love them. But they're just as selfish.

Years ago, I got a Bible for Christmas, a little one with a colored cover picture of Christ with a lap full of little children. A Bible, a pair of striped socks, and a green tie— a fake one with a fat knot and a clip on one end. Selfishness made me pout that day, sitting there on the floor at the foot of a white-flocked tree, while around me my older sisters' faces lit up with every new unboxed slip or sweater. Jealous, I was, of their joy.

"What are all those old coats doing on the sofa?" my Dad said from his chair.

So what did I care if somebody left some old clothes

lying around?

"Maybe you'd better check," he said.

I stood from my squat and jerked a wool coat off a pair of bright chrome handlebars. My father had wedged a new 26 inch J.C. Higgins between the sofa and the wall, and in one quick moment that Christmas Eve filed itself into my memory as the epitome of a family Christmas.

The year before it was a baseball glove, a Rawlings, with my hero Eddie Matthews' autograph scrawled across the pocket. And today it's the memory of those selfish Christmas rituals that still sweeten my anticipation of the season.

That was more than twenty years ago. The socks are long gone, the tie is hopelessly out of style, the bike is rusted into oblivion, and the glove, like Matthews himself, has been replaced by successive generations of mitts with successive generations of autographs. Only the Bible remains. I found it just recently, and I tried to give it to my daughter. "This belonged to your Dad when he was little," I told her. She thought that was interesting, but she kept toying with her Etch-a-Sketch. She was as thrilled as I had been that Christmas past, I suppose. Too bad selfishness doesn't wear out.

Perhaps it's the child in me that feels sad this Christmas season, the selfish child. I won't be going home this Christmas. We won't be opening presents in that same living room, we won't be munching peanuts and malted milk balls from mother's silver serving dish, and we won't be eating warm turkey sandwiches in the afternoon twilight. I'll miss all of that this year, and it's selfish of me, perhaps, to miss it.

It's selfish because home is—and I dislike admitting this—a state of mind. No one can really return to a state of mind. Almost thirty years ago already Grandpa died; I don't remember him being around the tree with the rest of us, but likely as not he's there in my sisters' memories of the day. Grandma's been gone for several years, died just a few hours after a big Thanksgiving dinner. A decade ago my father opted to a phony tree, pre-assembled: no sawdust and no needles stuck like common pins in the

living room rug. Today there's a room full of grandchildren, including two kids of ours, and there's
snowmobiling and electronic games and a whole sleigh full
of changes in the Christmas rituals. Being home for
Christmas, in some ways, isn't really being home for
Christmas.

Besides, home, to my children, is our house, not their
grandfather's. For them, being home for Christmas doesn't
really mean being at their Grandma's—it means being
here. And, quite naturally, my wife doesn't have my
memories; for her, being home for Christmas doesn't mean
being with her in-laws. There isn't one of us, really, who
goes home for Christmas.

This Christmas season, with my childhood family miles
and years away, my wife and I will be creating memories
for our own children. And years from now our children
will be haunted, like their father is today, by the memories
of their own child-like selfishness in this very house,
become home, this Christmas.

And maybe this year my wife and I will buy our son a
bike and stuff it in some dark Christmas corner. But before
we show him, we'll let him sulk for awhile, make him think
himself neglected. Maybe we'll give him a Bible and a pair
of socks—he's too young for a tie. And then we'll remind
him, as my father did me, how important that thick book
with the soft cover really is.

But there will come a moment, I'm sure, when those little eyes will flash with happiness. And when they do, when
they sparkle with the reflection of Christmas lights, those
eyes will sing the joy of a kid's Christmas. Their joy will
take me there, back into the memory of my own
Christmas-best and back to my father sitting there
watching my eyes as my own fingers, years ago, tore red
paper from some new surprise. I'll see it all in my children's
eyes.

This Christmas in our own home, our own selfish
children will be our own most precious gifts. We'll live on
their joy. And once again we'll feel the truth of that tired
homily about giving and getting, the one our parents
preached to us, and the one we preach to our kids, and the

one that two decades down the road these same kids, today ecstatic over some gimmick toys, will preach to theirs.

I guess this year I'll stay home for Christmas.

Small Town Sin

My daughter's third-grade world is just plain crowded with believers. That's what she told us on a cold Sunday morning in October, on our way to church. She pulled her hands into her shawl and snuggled it up tight around her chin. "I don't think I know one person who doesn't go to church," she said, looking out at a street full of cars packed with Sunday-best passengers.

My wife and I stared at each other rather blindly, as if there were something profound in such an odd realization, something we couldn't quite get a handle on so quickly.

And it has stuck in me ever since that morning, one of those kid lines that haunts you, begging, like some odd dream, to be interpreted. Sometimes I know how frantic Nebuchadnezzar must have felt, trying to find somebody to put a finger on that strange dream of his.

At first I felt almost guilty, my daughter growing up in a world no broader than a peep-holed shoe box, a little town where one finds sin only under rugs and between lines. Her out-of-the-blue realization made me want to move away first thing Monday morning—pick up and leave a town plump-full of church goers, take the kids out some place where they can live among real pagans. After all, I was thinking, it's no good rearing kids in a cloister. I could imagine them at twenty-five, assuming that their real enemies were infidel neighbors who stubbornly argue for pre-palsarianism. Not knowing real sinners will stunt my daughter's growth, I thought—righteous me. How will she ever know what it means to be a believer, if all she sees around her are blonde-haired xerox copies? We got a problem here, I thought.

Of course, the map is peppered with small towns, places where people would disagree violently. What better place to bring up a child than in a covenant circle that spreads to the limits of my daughter's own little world? That's what they'd say. You want to nurture a child, do you? How about a place where every one of her friends builds the same model Noah's ark she does, a place where she hears the same rainbow promise explained the same way in a pretty much identical Sunday School room as everyone else in the third grade? How covenant-like. That's what some might say.

But still, for a time, it haunted me—the idea that we were rearing righteous mutants, kids totally oblivious to "the real world," the world of television adventure, Las Vegas excess, white drifts of cocaine, streets full of cheap booze and porno shops. Our kids grow up with unlocked doors and ungaraged bicycles in a town where you can't even buy a *Penthouse* magazine. Maybe it's not fair to them, I kept thinking.

Some time later, at a consistory meeting, I listened to the professions of faith of two young men, one of them a college student, the other a high school kid, both of them coming in on their own to state publicly what had become clear to them earlier—the fact that their lives belonged to God.

Consistory meetings can be great bores. Even worse, they often seem to wind their way around and around and lead nowhere, as if every little problem were a cul-de-sac with a barricaded exit. Budgets need to be made, some programs seem dying, and a couple of folks are steamed about something—again. There's no end to the ritual in a consistory room.

But that night, at least for an hour, the whole room glowed in the Spirit-fanned warmth of two young men, telling it all about themselves and their God. What happened that night with those two young men made the budget discussion seem no more important than lunch. Two young men spoke like disciples.

36

And it's not easy for them either, even if it should be. Almost twenty of us sat around the tables, watching and listening to two young guys tightrope on questions about Trinity and the meaning of the sacraments. That's bad enough. But then there's the testimony, the profession. It's enough to make a man sweat, having to be so open about this deep feeling, this belief that God himself has tucked you right into his care.

For the better part of a half hour it was brittle in that room. You could see it on the kid's faces. Sometimes a quiver inched along a bottom lip until it was chewed to hold back the tears.

Someone asked both of them about especially important times in their lives, times when God became as real as they were painting Him to be in their testimony. They answered, strangely enough, in a very similar way. Both of them had suffered broken bones in bad accidents. Both had spent some time on their backs, staring up at off-white, hospital ceilings. Both claimed that bad accidents made them sense that someone else controlled their lives; and in those moments a God they had known only through their parents suddenly stood front and center in their own lives.

After the meeting, I couldn't help thinking of my third-grade daughter and my first-grade son, both of whom don't know a soul in town who doesn't go to church, and I couldn't help imagining some frightful images of a scene which may occur some day in my life and theirs: the whirling red lights of the rescue squad, the wail of a siren, the white emergency room. I thought of the parents of those two young men, standing there together a few years ago, crying, their sons broken bodies before them. It makes me want to lock my doors and never let my own kids outside.

And yet, the testimony of those two young guys made very clear something I've known throughout my life: that all things work together for good for those who love God.

The parents of those young men, on those horrifying nights, probably whispered it to themselves, their own professions of faith, right there in anguish and fear, in a sinful, broken world, in the same town where my daughter doesn't know anyone who doesn't go to church.

If one could pick up sin with a tweezers and flick it away, one would. If sin were only a liquid sloshing around in a bottle, it could be poured out in the sand. If sin lived only between the covers of a book or a magazine, even a writer would light a torch.

But sin is something else altogether, and it's in Sioux Center, Iowa, because it's in us, everyone of us, as surely as the throb of pulse through our wrists. We don't need Charles Mansons to give sin shape.

Whether or not my daughter ever meets someone who doesn't go to church, she will know sin. She already does. It's in the pain of the dentist's drill, in his warning about candy. It's in the way her eyes narrow and flash when she feels somehow less favored than her little brother. It's in her already, because it was in her father and her grandmothers and an album full of now long-forgotten photographs of those grand patriarchs and matriarchs we sometime think were glowingly beyond its grasp. Sin is there in every Bible story she'll ever read.

But somehow her great heavenly Father will find a way to make it all turn out, even when her earthly father can't—or won't understand. Even through car accidents, and the blood and broken bones. That's what her mother and I will have to spend our lifetimes telling her, no matter where she lives.

This Thanksgiving I'm thankful for my blessings—for our blessings, all of them. But this Thanksgiving, I'm even thankful for two bad accidents, even if there are four parents I know who would find it difficult to say it as easily as I will. I'm thankful to a God of blessing, but I'm even more thankful that this great God of ours can translate a curse into a sweet song of praise.

Bingo

Recently the checkers at the grocery store where we shop started handing out free bingo cards. They usually stack a couple of green stamps on top of my loose change, but lately they've been adding a token to play the promotional bingo that some sales exec is betting will entice me into the place more often.

"Hang that bingo card in front of their noses," he probably argued in a sales meeting, "and you'll have customers coming in three times a day. Once they're in, no telling what they'll buy." Likely as not, he had a computer screen full of market research to back his proposal.

If the bingo card is a carrot, then I'm not altogether comfortable in my role as a mule, even if that wily grocery exec —like American television—keeps insisting that a jackass is an apt caricature. H.L. Mencken, it is said, once claimed that no one ever went broke underestimating the intelligence of the American people. Our grocery store is merely following a long and highly valued tradition in American life, a tradition that casts me, Joe Consumer, as the consummate sucker. "Here, take a bingo card along home." Sure, I say, why not? They're free.

Last Saturday I saw a respected member of our church community staring up at the winning numbers posted on the wall above the empty pop cans. I was shocked, I guess, to see him hungrily checking the numbers, hoping to win. Maybe I shouldn't have been—we've got bingo cards too.

I suppose that seeing him looking to win reminded me of Fourth of July celebrations in the town where I spent my childhood. Every Fourth the entire town would turn out to the village park for the doings, and part of the doings was a raffle.

The American Legion sold little bundles of tickets—dime apiece in books of ten—threw the stubs in a concrete mixer, all day long pulled them out one at a time, calling winning numbers, then gave away the little prizes donated graciously by local businesses: a grease and oil job at the corner gas station; a carpet sweeper from the hardware store; a Monopoly game from the Variety Store. The Fourth of July raffle made people happy.

All afternoon the good folks would listen to the numbers called over the P.A. The lucky ones would stop their chatting, get on up, then stroll over to the raffle tent, check in their stubs, and pick up their quart of turpentine or two-pound hunk of cheddar, maybe buying a fudge bar to celebrate before heading back to the picnic table.

I could never buy tickets. My father wouldn't let me.

But it was no tragedy when I was little; a wad of tickets was no prize at all when compared to the red wax lips you could get for throwing a hoop around a milk bottle. But when I got older I started to wonder why that raffle tent was off limits—after all, the Legion Post was named for my Grandma's brother, a doughboy killed in France in late summer, 1918. I couldn't believe it was sinful for me to support the Legion.

My father said it was wrong because it was gambling. Not many other fathers seemed to think so, but my father did.

A few years later, what started to burn me up was not being a part of the drama of the final drawing. At 10:00 a couple of firemen would send up a sky-full of fireworks that cast alternating glows of pinks and blues and greens, like a magical snowfall, over the park grass where everyone sat oohing and aahing with their chins up. But once the last extravaganza was fired, most people rushed to the raffle tent for the last drawing—the last of the big prizes.

Maybe it was the most exciting event in that small town all year; at least it was the most public exciting event.

Who would take home the snowblower? Who would win the cement mixer? But even then, in those waning moments of the big celebration, I felt an itchy guilt just standing there, as if my interest in who would win was something close to sin itself. I could stand and wait with all the others, only because I was sure my father wouldn't be there to see me.

Luck, my father said, was something people shouldn't play around with. Not only did gambling build an expectation that something—even soap pads—could be had for nothing, but gambling messed around in an unseemly way with a Biblical doctrine that he felt worth keeping—the sovereignty of God. It was my father's Calvinism that kept me from buying tickets, and ever since I've been old enough to understand that commitment, I've respected him for it.

Providence is a whale of a big doctrine—too big for people to play with, my father said. A roll of dice tempts us to fool around with God's direction in our lives; a hand of cards can lead, like marijuana, to much darker evils. Soon enough we start thinking that something blind, like fate, is really steering our course. Luck, my father insisted, was not a word for any Calvinist to use—not ever.

And yet, luck or fate or fortune seems as much a part of our lives as annual community fests. Recently I saw a newsreel of Martin Luther King delivering his famous "I Have a Dream" speech at the Poor People's March in Washington more than twenty years ago. What struck me about King's behavior was the very hurried way he left the podium the second he had finished. He looked around as if he were concerned that he be able to escape easily; he was not in the least transfixed by the sheer power of the speech he had just given—as I thought he might have been. Yet, he had just delivered his most moving and memorable lines.

Of course, King could not have guessed that very speech would be his own enduring legacy. Sitting in some lonely motel room composing, he certainly didn't know that those eloquent phrases would eventually write themselves in a nation's conscience. Yet, they did.

Today, we could study that speech rhetorically; we could mark its emotional heights with a red pen and try to discover why those words became the armaments in the national battle for civil rights. But we'd not find the reason in syntax or diction.

"I Have a Dream" has become the enduring legacy of Martin Luther King for reasons beyond the control of King himself. If the Poor People's March hadn't been the first of many mass marches on the nation's capitol, if King hadn't been as successful as he was in creating a public consciousness of racism, if the moment itself weren't right for those exact words at that exact time, "I Have a Dream" would be but one more exotic line penned in a speech some researchers might find in a library, years down the road. It's a jarring thought but nonetheless true that King's own death has contributed significantly to the lustre of those words.

Martin Luther King wasn't gambling when he spoke that day, but he was as subject to forces beyond his own control as the Nevada tourist wrestling with a one-arm bandit. Midwestern farmers, playing their grain on the market, gamble as thoughtfully as they can, but they gamble nonetheless. A juvenile commits petty larceny. Rather than throw the book at him, we choose to slap his wrist with probation, gambling that such jurisdiction will be the right means to control the direction he's going.

We don't know what will happen because we can't know, so we gamble that our best shot will bring us closer to where we want to be. Gambling is a part of everyone's life: the parent who allows his children to walk to school gambles that no cruising predators will do the unthinkable; students gamble a four-year college education preparing for a career they hope they will be able to enter and enjoy.

And yet such hopefulness is not the same as the Fourth of July raffle or the slot machine or the state-controlled lottery or our grocery store's bingo cards—even though they are supposedly free. We gamble our grain, our time, our hope, and our love in the firm confidence of faith itself, the belief that "all things work together for good to them that love God." Gambling with life, in the promise of that commitment, is an act of faith.

Gambling, without that assurance, is a form of idolatry; it erases God-consciousness and vaults Lady Luck into the position of Sovereign. A belief in blind fate obliterates our sense of God's providence, and locks Jehovah God into church and out of the operation of daily lives.

"He that dares to confine the King to heaven," Thomas Fuller wrote, "will soon after endeavor to depose him and fall at last flatly to deny him." Fuller probably never bought raffle tickets.

Providence convinces us of the necessity of our need by assuring us of God's firm hand in our lives. King had no way of knowing that "I Have a Dream" would resonate through the years the way it has, and the image of his hurrying from the podium illustrates the complicated mysteries of our lives, mysteries known only to God.

Luck or fate, if we may use those words, keeps us humble in the face of power that is greater than our own. Nothing topples our pride like witnessing events in our lives that occur outside the borders of our own control. When confronted vividly with our own limitations, we feel awed by a power greater than our own. Christians located that power in the Creator.

Shakespeare's Hamlet finally reaches a maturity when he can look back upon his own indecision, then forward into time, and admit that there's a "divinity that shapes our end."

The danger of the bingo card is that we forget the truth of God's sovereignty. Forgetting that is forgetting God.

Babylon: or, Coming of Age at the State Tournament

The year was 1965. Madison, to a couple thousand high small-town Wisconsin boys, was Babylon. Milwaukee was our vision of a big city, but Madison was mythical, seductive, our vision of a fantasy land outside anything any of us had ever experienced.

But that was all part of the charm, really. It was part of the glory of the special reprieve given to varsity basketball players—two whole days off from school, a room in some family home, hours and hours of basketball, and Madison. Somehow, going to Madison made having already lost our own bid to get into the tournament seem forgettable.

We packed up our shaving gear and—at mothers' insistence, fresh underwear—slipped on our penny loafers, and then threw on the sacred robe—the red and white letter jacket, glittering gold metals hanging in clusters on the chest, chenille chevrons, one atop the next, lined up beneath our '65 and '66 as perfect as a fine formation of geese.

It was 1965, and we'd hang around the cavernous Fieldhouse, each with an identically patterned scarf, each with leather gloves jammed in our jacket pockets, each with a haircut like the guy on American Bandstand—the all-American variety of the street gang. We were cool, and we knew it because when we looked at everybody else, they all looked exactly the same.

That year three of us Oostburg boys stayed a good half hour's walk from the Fieldhouse. We never took a bus because we had no idea how much it cost or even how payment was made. We wouldn't stand the humiliation of having to appear that we didn't, by nature, know such things.

And it was cold that March; sometimes we'd pull our fingers in from our gloves and wish we were square enough to wear mittens. It was too cold for the snowballs we'd stopped throwing when we left the eighth grade, the same year we sold our bicycles in the neighborhood shopper.

It was 1965, and to a kid from rural Wisconsin, born and reared in a town like Oostburg, Vietnam was still a national test of manhood, racial riots were something blatantly un-American, and 1968—Kennedy, King, Detroit, Chicago—was still three incredibly long years away. We lived in a world as tight and strong as a gold class ring.

But Madison was Babylon.

We met our hostess at the door after the first session of games. She noticed the "Dutchmen" imprinted in bold red and white on the backs of our jackets. We told her it was the name of our team; we really had no idea that we were Dutch ourselves, growing up as we did with no one who wasn't.

"I've never been to Oostburg," she said. We loved telling her about it, because somehow it reminded us of being there. But we would have admitted homesickness about as quickly as fear.

She was a sweet woman, as I remember her, her hair silvery, soft, more glowing than either of my grandmothers', always combed neatly. But her husband had gone away, she told us. We laughed about it a little to ourselves, but we were sure that no grandparents ever had marital problems. We sometimes wondered about him.

But it was a fine brick house, nothing outlandish, just sturdy and square, and it stood on a corner of a street that could have been one of ours—tall elms, skeletal in March, of course, and other older homes like hers, some frame, two-story places not very different from my own. It seemed odd that she should live in Babylon.

Come to think of it, there were some strange paintings in her living room, long, thick swipes of paint on huge canvases that spanned whole walls. We weren't used to that. None of us could remember the kinds of pictures our parents had on our walls at home, but we were sure that they were nothing like these.

For two whole days the lady acted like a mother, and frankly, we were surprised, not really having known any city people before her, except relatives. Although we didn't see her that often, we did speak to her before we left in the morning, and she acted very nice, even giving us orange juice in tall glasses. She certainly didn't have to do that. No one else's hosts were that gracious.

"My husband loves basketball, especially the state tournaments. He usually watches them on the TV," she told us that final morning, Saturday. "He would love to be here tonight for the finals, I'm sure." She motioned us to take a chair before leaving for the Fieldhouse.

In our minds her husband had been a rather mysterious figure. The more we saw the lady, the more we thought of him as rather cold-blooded, deserting this sweet woman in early March. Often, when we were walking the two-mile trek to the Fieldhouse, we would guess at what the man did for a living and what he might be doing now.

"Probably a professor or something," Rog said, "goofing off someplace." "Insurance," Bob said, "at some convention in Baltimore or somewhere."

So when Rog asked her outright what her husband was up to, neither Bob nor I seemed too surprised that he would ask the question, seeing it would be the last time we could ask.

"Didn't I tell you?" she said. "He's in Alabama, with Dr. Martin Luther King. You have heard of King haven't you?"

I looked at Rog, and I saw his forehead drop over his eyes like an old sagging roof. And I knew why—King was an enemy, even though all we knew about blacks was the basketball glory of Milwaukee's inner city powerhouse, Lincoln High. The fact was, to us anybody who marched with King had to be communist, especially if he were white.

It was something we had never questioned at all. It was something as true as the precision of the Monroe

Cheesemakers, the all-white team from down state. We accepted the idea as if it were etched on Moses' mountain tablets. Demonstrators, especially whites, who ran down south for civil disturbances had to be anti-American, had to be communists.

For a moment I forgot the tournament. None of us could speak. Finally, Bob said, "Sure, sure. Well, we got to be going now. Find the rest of the guys from Oostburg."

It was cold in Madison in March of 1965. The snow cracked beneath our feet as we marched down to the Fieldhouse, a path that had already become familiar on our way to the glory of high school athletics. We were quiet for a while, our hands clasped around the hard leather handles of our suitcases.

"Old man must be a communist," Rog said. Any of us could have said as much.

I didn't say anything, but I knew somehow that two separate worlds were in danger of colliding right in my head, and I felt some kind of fear then, fear because one of those worlds was so new and indistinct and threatening —fear because I had no idea what would happen to that sweeter world I had always felt comfortable in, even loved —a world of letter jackets and class rings, of truths as sure as class mottos.

An Oostburg High School bus took us home after the tournament, home from Babylon. But today, sixteen years later, I don't for the life of me remember much about that final game.

The Testimony of History

Somewhere in a folder of my old high school papers there's an essay I once wrote about Vietnam. Handwritten in fancy, sophomoric script, little bubble circles for dots above the i's and elegant tails adorning the g's, the essay speaks its mind regarding the admirable righteousness of U.S. military presence in a place that was, at the time, much less well-known than Selma, Alabama. When hawks are sanctified, doves become diabolical; the essay warns readers not to fall prey to the wiles of the leftist hippies who sought to bring this great country to its knees, those long-haired types whose platform was constructed on planks abhorrent to my own sixteen-year-old's conscience.

That was 1964. Six years later I was among 100,000 Vietnam protestors who stood around the White House and made hay in the city of Washington D.C. In a small-town boyhood, I had never seen 100,000 people in one spot before, but the Kent State shootings had occurred that week, and people (most of them young) from as far away as Iowa had come to harangue anyone who would listen on the phony sanctity of American militarism in a strange country that had become, in six years, an even more abundant source of news than Jerusalem.

Some may measure such drastic change as verifiable growth of spirit, the track record of a mature Christian conscience coming of age. Others may well lament the pathetic tragedy of a bearded victim of time's unruliness —the descent of a mind from Christian values to commie vices.

The judge is still out on Vietnam; some later generation will likely try to outline heroes and villains in the street wars of the late sixties. But the arguments themselves will live on long after the original participants are locked between the covers of some history text. Likely as not, some enterprising computer programer will create a Vietnam simulation for junior high school students, if it hasn't already been done.

Perhaps we are hopeless victims of our times. Perhaps each of us carries the diseases of our particular social malaise; each of us sees with glasses specially ground by the events of our own age. Students today are career-minded; students yesterday were more rebellious. Awaiting a new label, we still call today's kids members of the me-generation.

Perhaps my own history is nothing more than a lesson in the uninspiring realities of a life determined by forces and events far out of my own control. Perhaps all of us are sheep, herded in a congregate mass and sent in directionless flight by the sound of nothing more dangerous than a car horn. Simply, we are pawns of the historical forces around us.

Nobody really enjoys the role of pawn. We don't like being told we really have no will of our own—that all our actions are merely expressions of dominating forces carrying us, willy-nilly, in sometimes good, sometimes bad directions.

We are, after all, participants, even when we think of ourselves as bystanders. Not having marched in Washington does not mean that each of us who lived through that era didn't struggle with the arguments of the time. Being career-oriented doesn't mean one feels no appreciation for the great ideas of literature or the lessons of history.

My evolution from hawk to dove marks my life as typical of a consensus shift in the American war consciousness, a victim, perhaps, of what was happening around me. However, when that change occurred, I was thereby contributing to what Charles Reich romantically dubbed "the greening of America." In that way, my change was itself a creative act. Each of us participates in history individually.

Armed with the capacity of memory, each of us, therefore, becomes, whether or not we want to admit it, a historian, and the longer we live the more clearly we understand our callings. Each time we sing "Creator Spirit, by Whose Aid," I am reminded of the Navy Hymn, the riderless horse in President John F. Kennedy's funeral procession, and the whole story of the assassination, three long days of national grief. Tie-dyed T-shirts spark memories of almost hallucinogenic pop lyrics. Raised black fists still spell out the danger of hot ghetto streets, and *Strike!* remains in my mind a university word, despite what I know about people like John L. Lewis or the Teamsters.

As participants in our own culture, we carry its story ourselves, and we use its lessons most wisely when we think in covenant terms about where we've been and what we've seen. Time and time again, David alludes to history to ask for God's help: "Our fathers trusted in thee: they trusted, and thou didst deliver them" (Psalm 22). In Psalm 77 God's past help is recalled in alleviation of present distress: "I have considered the days of old, the years of ancient times." Psalm 78 is itself a textbook of covenantal history. The record of God's people stands for David as catechism, bringing him closer to what he often knows but feels ashamedly doubtful to express himself.

I was born long after the thirties, but the word "depression" creates instant images in my mind, images created in me by my elders: my grandfather, the blacksmith, both arms up on the table, crying openly about lacking the money to buy the essentials for his young family; prairie grasshoppers so ravenous they devoured onion greens, then burrowed into the ground to chew up the bulbs themselves. God's history plays in technicolor when its lines focus with my own covenantal family—when I know the grandmother who picked her children's Sunday clothes off the bed and saw the silhouette left in the dirt that had seeped into the house from the dust clouds blackening the skies over the long plains.

My understanding of the depression is most acute when I know that my own covenantal grandparents took refuge from the drought with the words of Habakkuk 3: "Although the fig tree shall not blossom, neither shall fruit be in the vines; the labor of the olive shall fail, and the fields shall yield no meat; the flock shall be cut off from the fold, and there shall be no herd in the stalls: Yet I will rejoice in the Lord, I will joy in the God of my salvation." Knowing that verse helps me feel those prayers and gives me understanding of their times, and, most importantly, a sense of God's work in our times. Like David, I am uplifted by such stories remembered.

When I know that Van Raalte lacked sufficient manpower to bury his dead that first winter in southern Michigan, I understand something about the strength and perseverance and commitment of God's people. When a strong man, a corporate executive, tells me of his two sons' horror in Vietnam, when he tells me how he sent them there with his firm belief in the cause, and when he admits, his eyes down on his open hands, that he was wrong, I know more about that time I remember so vividly myself.

When we fail to reflect on our own experience as Christian members of the society in which we live, we stop writing God's story of His image-bearers. When we fail to tell our children, and when our children fail to listen, we are sacrificing our own blessed heritage, but more importantly, we are neglecting the story of God's dominion over His people and His world. We are neglecting His covenant story, and, in the bargain, weakening the power of His promises.

If we romanticize too much, if we sweeten history into nostalgia, if we handily forget what we shouldn't, let the professional historians help us, guide us back to the facts.

But history will never be the source of inspiration it was to David if we fail to look back and remember, if we fail to see the hand of the God of our fathers in our own biographies. Then miserably we fail Him in a very covenantal way.

Breaking Away

It has been close to twenty years since I bought my first stereo—a big gray crate of a thing with twin speakers that swung out from the amp like a pair of wooden wings. It was an American-made beast, sturdy enough to haul around on a flatbed truck. I bought it used, a thin strip of paint already worn off the turntable where successive fingers had flicked the reject lever.

"What you want to buy that for?" my father said when I took it in the house. "You can hear the same junk on the radio without spending a dime for records."

My father—like all fathers—didn't understand. He didn't realize that when I lugged that monster up to my bedroom, and, with both hands, slipped a new record on the turntable, it was as if a sudden silent storm blew away an entire wall of the house and left my bedroom facing nothing less than the great world itself.

Part of growing up it was—breaking out of the gates of my father's authority and into the throbbing, rocking world of the American sixties. I know that now, almost twenty years later, when I flip through a box full of dog-eared albums I bought (despite my father's advice), the same albums he recently discovered in a dusty corner of his attic. I left them there years ago, part of the junk one leaves behind whenever he or she becomes a different person. These covers—and this music—document a change in my life as clearly as the notches in the closet door sill, where my father penciled in my annual growth.

California's sunny paradise is right here in this box: The

Beach Boys' Greatest Hits—two albums full of falsetto dreaming—and Jan and Dean in concert somewhere, just the two of them in rugby shirts, bopping through "Do Wah Diddy Diddy" while a couple thousand screamers punctuate the silliness. Back then, just a few bars of "Surf City" melted those three-foot Wisconsin snowbanks outside my bedroom window, turned the front yard of my mind into Malibu.

And there's all sorts of soul in the box: Aretha Franklin, Diana Ross and the Supremes, The Best of Sam and Dave. My bedroom stood fifty miles from the nearest black kids, those children my mother, from the security of our old Mercury, claimed to be so darling when we'd venture into Milwaukee for a ball game or some Saturday shopping. But up in my room, the swing meter of soul music taught me that John Phillip Sousa's Fourth-of-July cadence was not the last word in rhythm.

There's a white album cover with no blazing name and no glossy photo, as if the group who cut the record was already so big they had no need to market an image. They were, of course. In the sixties, the Beatles came through the open wall of that childhood bedroom, changing their sound as they and their fans matured—"She Loves You" to "Strawberry Fields" to "Rocky Raccoon," and then some. "Sgt. Pepper's Lonely Heart's Club Band" used to float me and the whole bedroom on some visionary river out of time itself, a lazy trip up from adolescent tension and the romantic rebellion that colors my memory of the whole era of violence and Vietnam. Today, my own children watch me sort these albums, and they pick up Magical Mystery Tour, convinced by the black walrus on the cover that this one with the cartoons is really theirs. Maybe it is.

And here's one that still makes me tingle—Marianne Faithful singing "Come Stay With Me." Back then such lightly suggestive lyrics torqued a boy-become-man's imagination in a way that the sexual sewage of much of today's music cannot—the difference, perhaps, between the edge of a cheerleader's skirt and black and white porn. Nostalgia is here in this box too, I suppose.

Flower children are well represented, counter-culture's

darlings in ribbons and beads. On a plastic disc lined with simple lyrics, a singer named, simply, Donovan brought the Haight-Ashbury spirit of beads and baubles to my small-town bedroom. And maybe it was that hulking bell of a woman, Mama Cass, who makes me think of the group named Mamas and Papas as San Fransisco's finest. "Monday, Monday" was a favorite song of a whole generation of us, a generation still too young to have worked hard or long enough to know what Monday meant to people wearing blue or white collars.

And Joan Baez and Pete Seeger are here, two ancient Hootenanny heroes, reclaimed from any of a hundred peace rallies, guitar-strumming reminders of how easily folks tossed around buzz words like "hawk" and "dove" in the middle of a society that wrestled with its own values.

In the sixties of my youth one could ride the rebellion in the air into adulthood, the way the lyrics ride the melody of "Strawberry Fields." One could pump up his altruism with an album like this one—Sly and the Family Stone—and just march downstairs to the den and tell one's horribly irrelevant father, "There's a permanent crease in your right and wrong," spewing lyrics like Bible verses. Or one could escape a family's tightness on a "Li'l Honda" or a "Surfin' Safari." Music, in the late sixties, was the medium and the message, and its frenetic rhythms and disgruntled lyrics took me out of my small-town bedroom prison the way Dorothy's dream zoomed her out of Kansas and into Oz.

But it's close to twenty years since I bought that stereo, and today my own children, wide-eyed, flip through the old, vibrant red and blue album covers, looking at the odd pictures—strange long-haired men strung with beads, or four buckskinned ruffians jammed in a bathtub, or a blond girl, her straight-hair flowing over her shoulders as she sits, Indian-style, on the floor of Carnegie Hall—the popular pose of a thousand kids in city parks from Long Beach to Passaic, bead-strung kids in T-shirts and scruffy hair, forever smoking something.

I'm older now, old enough to have learned that there was something of the Monkees-phenomenon in all of this flat plastic, something of American business trickery sucking up the whole counter-culture as if it were a toy to be specially marketed for December Christmas sales, turning John Denver, for a time a real counter-cultural hero, into little more than a Rocky Mountain High, changing Sonny and Cher into glittering Hollywood has-beens.

Life encloses us—all of us—in an endless series of childhood bedrooms, I suppose: first, the bedroom of parental dependence, then the bedroom of adolescent rebellion, and then, perhaps most tightly, in the bedroom of adult complacency—the comfortable assurance that now—now that I'm older—at long last I know absolutely everything there is to know. Living, I suppose, means always having to break away. Simply an inch of growth means that some clothes don't fit anymore; the boy or girl who used to wear them simply isn't what she or he was a year before. For every real moment of truth—those moments when we face up to something we didn't see before, those moments when our own needles jump from the methodical turning of our lives—for every one of those moments there is growth and change, whether it occurs at fifteen or fifty.

And the sad part is those changes don't come easily. I can imagine what my father thought, one floor below, the floor-shaking beat of the Rolling Stones rumbling through his den. These records never were his world, and he knew it. Just having the sound in his home must have riled him. I knew it then, but today, myself a father, I know the feeling even better.

Yet, there was, and is, a certain inevitability to all such value-shaking. My grandfather's life was not my father's, my father's will not be mine, and my children's will not be their father's. Sometimes, now, I wish it were not so.

Neither are our expressions of faith exactly the same. The differing cultures in which successive generations live shape the way we worship and the way we live as believers; an unruly gang of mop-heads like the Beatles forces us to change, drive our expressions of faith in directions my own God-fearing grandfathers couldn't have anticipated. Contemporary Christian music has attracted an army of believing kids, often with as raucous a beat as the Rolling Stones ever generated.

Sadly, such changes are frequently painful. Some of our grandmothers thought dancing an abomination; but those same ladies, along with their husbands, could be avowed racists in the easy-chair world of white, ethnic ghettos. More than likely, my own grandfather didn't always approve of the Big Band Sound my father sneaked an ear to. No matter what my parents thought of them, the Beatles were, for better or worse, part of the world that I had to confront, growing up in the sixties.

And yet, paradoxically, there is a certain firmness to faith, a certain eternal relevance that doesn't fade with each passing era. Few words John Lennon ever wrote will resonate through the years ahead with the ironic twang of his famous appraisal—perhaps true—that people thought more of the Beatles than they did of Jesus. Only a few years ago, a mindless assassin shot him cold dead in his own front yard. It's not easy to admit this about my old heroes, but the worn-out album covers affirm that faith's eternal relevance makes even the Beatles silly.

We own a stereo now, Japanese-made, with a skinny little arm so slight it almost floats over the old records' scratches. The round speakers are plastic.

But I haven't bought an album for years. I've got no idea how much they might cost today. It really doesn't matter, because buying albums doesn't make much sense when you can hear all you want on FM for free, at least that's what I tell myself today. It's strange—seems as if I've heard that before.

Sometimes, oddly enough, breaking away brings us right back into a neighborhood we might well have seen before.

On Winning, and Losing

"Up in the attic there's some old high school junk of yours," my mother says. "Why don't you look it over—see if any of it is worth keeping?"

A few chenille athletic letters, festooned in gold bars, some yellowed press clippings, a couple of black and white pictures, and a three-ring binder stuffed with papers—that's what is up here. So it's the teacher in me that sits cross-legged in the glare of a naked light bulb and leafs through the nearly twenty-year-old class notes, trying to discover just exactly what it was we did in high school other than play ball.

The answer is clear. The truth is scribbled in pen on faded, ditto hand-outs from English class, intricate systems of x's and o's—defensive alignments, zone presses, and picks and rolls—those are my recorded responses to a discussion of the Romantic Period in American literature. The fact is, in high school we didn't do anything but play ball. I've got the truth here in my hands.

Nathaniel Hawthorne never stood a chance against the likes of Joe Namath, and today I don't suppose he fares any better against Joe Montana. It's no great surprise to see pass formations pencilled in over my notes because it's no soul-stirring revelation to be reminded of the deep homage we pay to organized sports in America. The fact that some Texas university is more than willing to pay its football coach some two or three times the salary of a Nobel prize-winner isn't really shocking anymore because more universities, whether we like it or not, create images of themselves on the athletic field. Undoubtedly, scores of Northern beer drinkers could tell you that this year Clemson was number one in college football, but how many of them, bellied up to the bar, could tell you where the school is? How many Catholics care about what's being taught in the theology department at Notre Dame?

Everyone, even Howard Cosell, holds forth on America's obsession with sports. One hundred five million people watched Super Spectacular XVI from the Silverdome, the annual celebration *Time* called "a national, cultural and conversational imperative, if not a religious holiday." So I sit here, the history of my school days in my lap, and try to understand why so much time and energy and spirit are willingly sacrificed at the altar of some jockstrapped idol.

Somewhere in these notes I'm sure I can find the answer. It's a poem by a woman who never followed her team into the play-offs. Years later I noticed it, long after high school; but it will be here in these papers, unnoticed, lost behind a maze of pencilled-in offensive maneuvers.

> Not one of all the purple Host
> Who took the Flag today
> Can tell the definition
> So clear of victory

> As he defeated—dying—
> On whose forbidden ear
> The distant strain of triumph
> Burst agonized and clear!

Emily Dickinson understood sports, maybe as well as Roone Arledge. Winning. Victory—the thrill of it. That's what keeps us coming back, what creates in us such a voracious appetite for the excitement of competition. Winning is the psychological high whose very possibility saps the energy and spirit from high school kids and turns a novel like *The Scarlet Letter* into some dumb story about boring, old people who were really into religion. The possibility of an upset, of a chance to win, draws us back to the TV week after week, when we know—we're sure—

our team is a bona fide loser with a stupid bum for a coach.

But there's more to winning, and Dickinson knows it. Winning is made more glorious by the absolute agony of losing. Victory is thrilling *because* defeat is so blasted agonizing. A tie, is, as people say, like kissing your sister. Take away the spectre of losing, of having poured all your spirit and energy into the game and yet coming up short, and you destroy the euphoria of triumph. Picture a game where everybody wins and you'll see a field without a fan.

Only two teams tangle in a gym—one loses and one wins. Win and you ascend to glory; lose and you cast yourself into the stenchiest pit. There is no middle ground in competitive athletics, only the absolutes—win or lose. And from the moment some kicker with a foreign name sets the football on the tee, we know very well that one, only one, of two diametrically opposed outcomes will belong to us. That's the drama we watch. That's why some of us play.

Such is the nature of things in sports, but why are we so obsessed that four of the nine most watched television programs of all time are Super Bowls? Maybe there is an answer in these class notes, for I didn't fail that English class, despite the fact that the teacher's outline of the life of Ralph Waldo Emerson looks more like the coach's playbook. I still passed—shoot, yes!

Today, failure—real losing—is something we experience only in athletic competition. Sports is perhaps the only place where there is only black and white—only thrills and agony. Some say we live in a world where there are no rights or wrongs, where morality is but a matter of legislation passed by the latest session of Congress, where anything goes—if it feels good, do it. If there are no wrongs, there can be no rights. If there is no failure, there can be no excellence. There is nothing but the gray of middle ground; nothing but a bunch of ties—and there's little excitement in constantly kissing one's sister.

We may have banished the agony of failure from our lives today, but the thrill of victory stepped out a side door at the same time. There's no report card with this junk, but I probably received a B in English.

For us, absolutes exist only in athletic competition. Maybe that's why we watch Super Bowls so passionately. And miracles exist only in a world with absolutes. IBM's best computers, Las Vegas's most crafty odd-makers, CBS's most gifted commentators may well guess wrong when Joe Namath leads a lowly Jets team to an impossible Super Bowl victory. An upset is nothing more than fulfillment of a hope beyond reason. An upset is a miracle, and we are too skeptical to believe in miracles—except in sports. So games draw us in droves, as fans, as viewers, as contestants—all for a taste of sweet, sweet victory.

Here's an old baseball I grabbed after we won the conference championship. We were tough in baseball my senior year, I remember. We were decent in football; but basketball—what an embarrassment!

And here's *Moby Dick* too; the binding is barely cracked. If I'd have read it then, I'd probably have thought that Captain Ahab would have made a heckuva coach.

Maybe I'll keep it. And the baseball—I can't throw out the baseball.

We, the Vietnam Spectators

Vietnam never laid a hand on me; I never saw a rice paddy or walked the Saigon streets, or awakened to the thwacking rush of Army helicopters. I've never stumbled through a jungle. The shape of Cambodia I remember only from the map Richard Nixon pointed to in May of 1970.

But neither did I go to jail or leave for Canada, or sugar my urine or brace my teeth or make any other attempt to avoid Vietnam. Nobody ever begged me to return home years later; neither President Ford nor Carter ever offered me amnesty. I was, throughout the entire era, little more than a spectator.

We still live, all of us, in the shadow of that era, even those who, like me, bear no visible scars. Just recently, I framed the cover page of an old student newspaper and hung it on my wall—five clenched fists boldly underlined with one word, "Strike."

It's an artifact now, a symbol of an era that has slipped into the objective past of a whole new generation of college students, already part of a nation's history and, therefore, of little more than passing interest to an undergraduate busily preparing himself for one of life's marketable skills. That clenched fist has lost its grip on America's emotions; today it needs a footnote.

But subconsciously Vietnam is still with us, all of us, even those it passed by. Spectators take their thrills vicariously and thereby keep their knees intact. But the memory of a rough game stays with them. Whether we went to Canada or Saigon or we stayed home, Vietnam, for all of us who grew up in the late sixties, is more than a memory.

For those of us who didn't go, "Where were you during Vietnam?" is more a pointed question of honor than of simple information.

And our answers invariably carry some supplemental narratives to verify the fact that we were alive at the time: "We were here, but we marched." Somehow, it doesn't matter. We took neither the supreme act of loyalty and went to Southeast Asia, nor the supreme act of conscience and went to jail or Canada. For many of us spectators, the 4-F—in 1970 the classification of freedom—has become, years later, the badge of failure it was meant to be. Today, the 4-F triggers a sense of guilt for not having been to either Vietnam or Canada.

In the spring of 1968, on the night Lyndon Johnson opted out of the presidential race, I was among hundreds of sunburned northern college students wriggling away at a dance on Daytona Beach. In May of 1970, I told my college baseball coach that my marching against the war meant more to me than catching a Saturday double-header, and I left for Washington. The token scars I bear from that era lie no deeper than a skipped double-header. So high, for me, honor soared.

But I remember the almost vicious sense of righteousness in the eyes of a Navy vet who came home early in 1967, convinced that anything less than a full offensive in Vietnam was cowardly and defeatist. He had no toleration for argument. Vietnam turned his spirit to stone. And I remember the bloodied knuckles of a roommate in 1969, a vet whose adjustment to home staggered through long nights of drinking and fighting. Vietnam blessed him with an appetite for action that straight-life in small-town Iowa couldn't satisfy. His memories wouldn't let him sleep. These were the real scars of Vietnam.

A decade later I sat alone in an armchair late one night and watched two of my peers, two 30-year-old drunken Vietnam vets hugging and crying like children, as if all of it—the dope and the death, the absolute lunacy of a war few of them wanted to fight—as if all of it had ended just a

week before. And I sat there trying my human best to em-
pathize. It was all I could do as an outsider.

We all share in the guilt over Vietnam—the hawks, the
doves and even the spectators. For those who watched, a
decade later it's the spectre of not having lived—at least of
not having headlined, at most, not having suffered.

The agony and the torment, the courage and the
selflessness belong to those who acted, either out of obe-
dience or disobedience—and not to those who watched.
We have no answers to where we were during Vietnam,
and our muteness today is an odd kind of cross in itself.

Perhaps, at a decade's distance, we can call this odd guilt
some rugged masculine urges left sheathed and unsatisfied.
Perhaps it's the guilt of having been passive in an age that
demanded action. Perhaps it's only the army legacy of the
4-F classification. Whatever it is, it stings some of us today
when we watch films like *Apocalypse Now* or read books
like *Going After Cacciato*. Vietnam was an era that, for
better or worse, belongs to the other guys, even though we
were there.

In August of 1970, I lived just outside Madison, Wisconsin and had just begun my first year of teaching when the
blast at the Army Research Center on the University of
Wisconsin campus shook windows all over town and
killed an innocent graduate student. It was the end of the
days of the romantic rebellion in this country, and I knew
it. The war itself would be over in a matter of time and a
few thousand more lives.

I had seen it all, from the beginning—from the days of
the military advisers, the days when the cloak of com-
munism was laid over the backs of the first dissenters,
through the Gulf of Tonkin Resolution and the Cambodian
incursion, to Kent State, a dead research chemist, and a
pitiful, hasty retreat from Saigon; and all of it through the
pall of far too many thousand American and Southeast
Asian war dead. But the story belonged to the
others—those who acted.

This is the scar of my Vietnam days, my guilt. This is
where I was during Vietnam, and where it's left me today,
ten years later.

On Learning, and
Teaching, Identity

In 1966 just about everyone went to church on Sioux Center Sunday nights, including just about everyone in the dorm. Everyone, almost. It's far enough behind me now that I dare confess how we hid from the RA's when the heels of their penny-loafers clicked down the linoleum hallway, or how we snuck away sometimes already at five —maybe a whole carful of us—took off to some pizza barn fifty comfortable miles from the rigid Sabbatarianism of northwest Iowa's Dutch Calvinists.

It was another world out there in Sioux Falls. Some Dakota girl would take our orders and never even hiss at our skipping church. She wouldn't blink if we'd order beer, and we guessed she knew nothing at all about the college —and the culture—we were escaping for a few Sunday hours.

Acknowledged reprobates we were, proud that out there—a world away from post-church Sunday dorm hymn sings—we were claiming an identity far different from all those dainty Bible-toters back in the dorm. Our own adolescent rebellion, fueled by national brawls over Vietnam and civil rights, made us grab the lapels of our own faith tradition and push it away like some wimp in a double-breasted suit.

On those Sunday nights we sinned, at least against a culture. And I remember the mutant emotion when we sat there over pepperoni and mushrooms—something of guilt and something of liberation—and watched all the other customers so happily engaged in having a good time. It was a different Sunday world, and we loved the maddened rush of freedom, of not being where we had forever been on eighteen years of bone-dry Sunday nights.

Such delicious sin it was. And an odd paradox that anything wrong could feel so good. You sometimes wonder how much Romeo would have loved Juliet if his love hadn't been so richly forbidden.

But it was forbidden, and so in 1966 was skipping church, and Sunday night pizza, and beer. But it seems to me now that such dastardly sins against the Dutch Calvinist ethos did more to define the edges of that culture for me than the world's longest unbroken string of Sunday School attendance. We cannot distinguish the nature of our own identity without viewing ourselves in contrast with those we are not, and it seems to me now that such quick, guilt-ridden breaths of Sunday freedom in a dim-lit pizza shack have allowed me to relax today within an only slightly modified Dutch Calvinist culture—the one I now claim as my own.

Life in a hall of mirrors creates a double distortion: we believe that everyone else looks as we do; and we think we look like everyone else. Without some image alien to our own visions of self, we cannot really know who we are. And so the dog in the fable forgot he mouthed a bone, until, sadly, he saw in his reflection a dog who did. We recognize ourselves by our opposites. We define by constrasts already set within us. And thus our experience outside our culture can define and even affirm the nature of our own identities.

James Joyce, it is said, allowed his devout Irish Catholic mother to die in fear for her son's soul. On her deathbed, she asked her unbelieving son to partake once more in the mass—just for her. Initially, Joyce assumed that going through the motions would hurt no one, but he refused, finally, claiming that the mass was too heavily charged with meaning for such cheap deception. On that day, in his unbelief, he was among the greatest of believers; he was, from the outside, honoring the sacrament more deeply than those parishoners who, as if by instinct, were herded through the celebration. Neither Joyce nor Sunday night church-skipping need be made heroic, but the parallel is clear: outside the faith, Joyce may have seen the rituals of his boyhood faith defined more clearly than he ever had before.

A decade ago I taught high school English in a rural high school, a recently consolidated district of beautifully sloping hills, clean Wisconsin dairies, and two rival villages, neither of them having a dominant church. Just six months out of Sioux Center at the time, I asked my senior class to respond to Bacon's "On Marriage and Single Life." Somehow the discussion shifted to divorce, and their attitudes shocked my Calvinist sensibilities. Not one of those rural students thought divorce was wrong. "If you can't live with her—you better get out of the relationship"—that was their sentiment, all of them. That night I rode home alone and knew what it was to be reared as a Dutch Calvinist, because I knew the ethos of my students was not my own.

Experience is life's fine mesh. No theory, no doctrine, no ethic is really set until it has been tempered by life's experience; and no matter how diligently we work at setting it deep within young people, finally they themselves will have to lock it in place. As educators we can hope our curricula have adequately prepared them to confront such experience. As parents we trust our example and our admonition will serve our children well. As believers we can have faith that our way is in them. But most of our kids will meet experience that tests them—and through them, us—someday; almost all of them will be forced to measure what they are by standards we haven't given them or have tried to keep from them, despite the depth of our devotion and the relevancy of our strategies. Experience will try them and our standards within them, just as it tries us, over and over again—yesterday, today, and tomorrow.

A man from Michigan, an alcoholic, once told me that the catechism he had learned as a child never meant anything to him—not until he walked into his first AA meeting and read the "steps" on the wall. "I looked up there and all I saw was 'sin, salvation, and service,' " he said. Experience shook the dust from his years of training and left him with a method of seeing himself and his problem in the shadow of his confession, the creed he had recited as a child. The man's identity, mute until then, still emerged to serve him well.

And there was another man, a farmer who lost his young son in an accident. He loved the catechism, claimed he always did, even when he was a boy himself. But when his own child was killed—when he carried that lifeless body—the sovereignty of God, the Calvinism of his youth, leaped center stage from a background of dim abstraction. First he questioned it—the sturdy confidence that somehow God was in control of all of this—and then, slowly, he resigned himself to the reality of his son's death within the framework of God's control. "That knowledge has got to be there," he told me. "You've got to have those answers ready."

Sometimes we teachers take ourselves far too seriously. Finally, we can do only so much. No Dean of Students, no fastidious RA, no pious professor of theology could have kept us from Sunday night pizza. No one of us keeps our students from the experience they will seek and find. Even Joyce's mother couldn't keep him in the church.

We have all we can do to pump them full of the facts of their identity. They are children of God, not ants being trained for some prescribed task in the anthill, not mice being conditioned for response, and not machines designed to carry out society's commands. We are image-bearers, and so are they. We are, all of us, stamped with God's own identity.

And we are, all of us, heirs to related traditions. We have last names, we carry ethnic flavors, and we are members of faith communities. No Christian lacks identity.

Let it be our task to teach them that identity, then pray they'll hold it when experience blesses them with the kinds of lessons educators can only toy with.

We all should remember that although the significant experiences of a person's life do not take place within the classroom, the very marrow of man's being is shaped and strengthened by a knowledge of history and science, the ability to use and appreciate the power and beauty of language. These skills, for the most part, come only from formal education.

As parents, teachers, and church leaders we create an image of identity that students will finally accept, or modify, or reject. We cannot, in any number of years, mold that identity into their conscience or force it into their accepted code of behavior. Life itself, the experience God grants them, will shape what they accept as their heritage and their identity, as it has our own.

Seagulls and Sovereignty

I didn't grow up on Lake Michigan, literally. My ethnic ancestors first set claims on the Lake Michigan shoreline, and they called their first American town their own "Amsterdam," hoping, perhaps, that the name would provide some clear identity and maybe a touch of security in the new country. Today there is no Amsterdam, Wisconsin—no town, no streets, no church. When the railroads came twenty years after its founding, my ancestors' oxen lugged Amsterdam up and away from the shoreline on long tamarack boughs, setting it carefully down a mile away, close to the new shiny rails, sure that growth was inevitable over there, adjacent to the freshly cut path of the great steam locomotive.

They were right, of course. So today, 125 years later, the shoreline belongs to people who have made their fortunes in Milwaukee or Chicago, people whose names once seemed foreign to the Veldbooms, the Wilterdinks, and the Eernisses, the later generations of the first settlers. In 1850, the first Dutch immigrants knew nothing at all about the real estate market, so they turned their backs on the shoreline, moving west into soggy Wisconsin marshlands, where they put to use their old-country propensity for tiling and draining the swamps and turning it all into productive farmland.

So when I say I grew up on Lake Michigan, I mean I grew up close enough to hear its continuous roar through my open bedroom window, close enough to ride my 26 inch J.C. Higgins down to the beach and go skinny-dipping, one fairly comfortable mile from the sharp steeple of the Dutch Calvinist church where we all went to catechism on Saturday mornings.

I grew up on Lake Michigan the way some people grow up on meat and potatoes. In high school we'd pair off, snuggle up in our cars at the end of the lake roads, and "park"—a wonderful teenage euphemism, today probably thought to be some kind of archaic usage. Every spring we'd seine for smelt in chest-high waders, and in the winter I remember driving old cars down miles of frozen sand. Annually there were those few golden weeks in August when Lake Michigan would warm to a tropical 68 degrees, and everyone would go in, confident that Bermuda had nothing on southwestern Wisconsin and our own big lake.

On hot summer nights we'd barefoot the wet shore, the continuous ebb and flow of lake waves as refreshing as a quart jar of icy lemonade after twenty acres of baling hay, its peaceful lapping as firm and reassuring as Christmas in a little Dutch Calvinist town. Often, it brought out the best in us, a walk like that, for you can't talk trivia when your footsteps have been forever erased a moment after you've left them. There was something there on the beach like that. Perhaps it's that kind of mystical presence that makes me say I grew up on Lake Michigan, as if she, or he, shaped me as surely as the smooth driftwood it offers up during every season of the year.

It's that kind of mystical presence I want my children to feel when I bring them to the shoreline now, years later, a time when too much of the beach is now sentried by bright yellow "No Trespassing" signs. But we go anyway, though it's the middle of winter.

In winter the beach is desolate from the sharp grass of the sand cliffs to the hem of ice chunks the lake wears until March. The sand runs smooth and true as plate glass, and the tiny footsteps my children make seem remarkable, the paths they form, poetic. In the winter the beach belongs to the wind, of course, uncovering stones as round and flat as silver dollars, rolling the soft sand in flowing drifts—"frolic architecture" Emerson called it—in elegance unmatched by anything manmade. Just the seagulls are here now—and the deer. My daughter puts two little fingers in the cloven prints they leave behind.

Just being here makes me confess hypocrisy, as if my real purpose in coming here were my children's benefit. Lake Michigan, this magnificent presence, still attracts me, still leaves me in awe, too full of the touch of its presence to explain it clearly. So while my kids write their names in the sand with the tail feather of a seagull, I let it work its mystery on me in its own inimitable, silent way, the way it always has.

It tells me things I've always known but never really taken the time to believe. Its incredible size mocks my own smallness. Its eternal rhythm reveals the transience of my own life and mocks my ambition. Filling the entire eastern horizon, its immense presence portrays what Thoreau called the "quiet desperation" of my daily living.

And yet, paradoxically, it strengthens me amid all this humiliation. I am reminded, Calvinist that I am, of the interdependence of the sand and the water and the gull and the deer and the sky; and within it all, my self, man, God's final creation during that first incredible week, this lake, somehow, still remembers. My children's meandering paths only emphasize the lesson, because they fit in too. I don't remember it, but there must have been a time when I, like my children, looked at all of this as just the world's greatest sandbox.

We all need our Lake Michigans. Novelist John Fowles says he feels it most in the forest, this inescapable sense of having to measure oneself and one's ambitions in the face of the eternal. I was brought up on the lake; I feel it here. When I see my father-in-law's eyes sweep up over 40 acres of soybeans and scan the horizon of Iowa farmland, I know he feels it too.

My daughter says her hands are cold, so we head back to the car. It is time, I suppose. That's when I soften enough to forgive those first Calvinist settlers who knew that the beach could grow no corn, who left the beautiful shoreline to today's "beautiful people." I can forgive because I learned from them another of those fretful paradoxes of faith: having been awed by His presence, He tells me to go back now, to leave, to return to the world of quiet desperation. It's a command. It's not a request. Eventually it gets hard to breathe on a mountaintop. The beach, no matter how beautiful, is as sandy as a desert. Such is the nature of retreat; it is done only in order to return uplifted, strengthened, more sure, perhaps, of who we are, what we are about, but never as an end in itself, no matter how ravishing.

Out here, facing the vast horizon of perfect blues, its seam of sky and water barely visible, I find it easy to sing, "This is my Father's world." Back at the office, five floors up overlooking a skyline of a million human beings, it's not so easy, even though it is as true. Having been here, I know it once more.

After the car warms, my daughter asks if we can come back again sometime.

Sounds of Shattered Silence

Not long ago, around eleven at night, someone smashed a bald whitewall tire through our front windows. It showered glass over the living room rug, and shattered the wood lattice work of the old colonial crosspiece window, which probably has fronted the house since the Depression.

It was an act of vandalism, that colorful word derived from an awful tribe of "infidels" whose ruling passion was, supposedly, mindless destruction.

The person who did it was a vandal, an "infidel," someone whose understanding of human dignity begins and ends with himself. He did it in the presence of at least three other young people, friends, obviously, people he could trust to keep the secret of his identity from those who feel that vandalism is exactly what it means.

I live in downtown Oostburg. At night I watch the fair-haired children of good Dutch folk gather in groups of ten or twenty or thirty in parking lots directly across the road from our front windows.

Many evenings our living room is filled with the astounding vulgarity and profanity which dominates their sentences. The sound of their tires screams through our kitchen, even with the windows closed. Most mornings I watch the storekeeper's son across the road sweep up the glass from last night's brown disposable bottles, the grenades of 20th century American vandals.

To some, Oostburg is a prison. Downtown Oostburg is home to many of the community's elderly, and they, too, live with vandalism, profanity, outright defiance of the law.

And they are afraid, afraid of whitewall tires crashing through front windows too expensive to replace on fixed incomes, afraid of being abused verbally like old man Elisha of the Bible, afraid of eggs or tomatoes or firecrackers, afraid, just plain afraid, tragically afraid.

Before the shattered window episode, the old people had warned me not to do anything about the hell-raising.

"They'll get you," they said. But I grew up in this village. It wasn't that long ago that I was a kid. Kids have families. I know the parents, the family church affiliations, the parents' work. These kids won't retaliate, I told the elderly; they're not that bad.

So I wandered out on the streets after midnight. The food store parking lot had turned into a raucous boardwalk, the street into a drag strip. Oostburg's main street was transformed into a Mardi Gras—Vander Mardi Gras.

I asked them for peace, and for respect, and for tolerance.

Then a bald whitewall smashed out my front windows.

So now I ask myself why. What causes vandalism in the age of wealth? What could prompt kids to act so much like "infidels?"

What has happened to peaceful Oostburg, the town whose 125-year history was forged by pious Hollanders seeking a new life based on their view of duty to God and His Kingdom?

What has happened to the idyllic town of well-kept lawns and neat homes and school lockers that need not be locked, where "outsiders" still feel the pressure to cut their lawns on Saturday, not Sunday?

What has happened to the family? Why is it that little Oostburg (population 1,650) seems not so dissimilar to New York City, its own elderly held hostage by its children?

Unless nostalgia paints history more vividly than its real portrait, Oostburg—one of Sheboygan County's Dutch hamlets, a village of churches, a village of parental schools—has not always allowed its 15-year-olds the luxury of drinking beer on the main street.

For decades Oostburg prided itself in its churches, its believers, its Calvinism, that body of doctrine which focuses with equal strength on the sovereignty of God and the depravity of man.

A hundred years ago no church patriarch would have called himself anything but a Calvinist. Even fifty years ago the churches of Oostburg were probably ruggedly Calvinistic. Today, perhaps, few of the people in Daane Hardware or at the Knotty Pine restaurant have any idea of what the word means.

Perhaps the ardor of belief has waned in Oostburg. In the drive for ecumenism, the doctrinal integrity and intellectual sharpness inherent in its pursuit have given way to the easy road of American evangelicalism, Sunday religion, "me and my sweet Jesus," or dead orthodoxy.

Oostburg's churches are still full on Sunday, but perhaps the community's shared interest in living a Christian life— a sanctified life—has died the same death as the old Reformation Day rallies on Oct. 31. That day now is owned by UNICEF, Sesame Street costumes and peanut butter kisses in orange and black wrappers.

Some kid broke our windows because he felt no spiritual motivation not to, no fear of hell, maybe, no sense of a Calvinist God watching the action, then noting it carefully in the Great Book.

Perhaps the family is to blame. Divorce was once the worst of words in Oostburg. Children were brought up with the firm conviction that time, prayer, and the Holy Spirit could cure any family disagreement. Divorce meant excommunication, and the church was one's community. Divorce brought misery.

Today, divorce rates are rising in Oostburg, as they are in every Oostburg of every state. But divorce is like hearing something scary in a dark forest without even seeing the grizzly. Marriage is in trouble. The family is suffering. Children are confused by misguided loyalties, by homes where love is a word on a K-Mart poster.

Maybe the whitewall is a request for recognition in a world where recognition is very hard to find.

Maybe it's money. Maybe both Marx and Jesus were right about the love of wealth. Most kids have cars today, it seems. Many of them have big cars that rumble down the streets with their rear ends up like some permanent obscene gesture. Most kids ride snowmobiles. Many kids have motorcycles.

Can it be fifty years since the Depression? Thirty-five since Hiroshima? Is our whole culture too fat? Do we even believe in ourselves as a nation?

Maybe kids have too much and want nothing but excitement, the kind of excitement which snowmobiles, cross country skis and motorboats all piled up together can't give them. Maybe the splintered glass of my front windows spelled out the fact that money, even lots of money, just isn't enough.

Why not blame the school? Everybody else does. Maybe if we felt, like the immigrants, that education was really important, our kids might think so, too.

Maybe if we really were convinced that education was more than just a means of securing a lucrative salary our kids might think so, too. Maybe if the kid had to study for an algebra test or finish writing a term paper, he wouldn't be on the street in the first place.

But there is more to say. The kid has smashed my windows with the decided notion that he'll not get caught, even though there were three witnesses.

There is a sad but true fact here: In the entire village of Oostburg, there probably are not more than ten kids bad enough, vulgar enough, evil enough to destroy property so willfully. Everyone here knows that.

In fact, there probably are quite a few residents who could list those ten without checking the latest high school yearbook. But the kid knows he won't get caught, even though half the town might know very well who he is. That's the way it is in this country. The old Calvinists wouldn't scream for justice; he'll get his reward, they'd say. Our windows are smashed because some bad kid knew very well he wouldn't get caught.

It is beyond my power to go on: television, alcoholism, drug culture, peer pressure—some of the old-liners might even blame the "outsiders."

Finally, however, the kid is to blame. His action has inflicted hundreds of dollars of damage to my house. The tire was thrown by him—not by his parents, his preacher, his father's pocketbook, his high school guidance counselor, or the American system of justice.

He is to blame—and it's quite likely that everyone ever involved with the kid would say, "It's not that we didn't try."

The next time Oostburg's downtown turns riotous, I suppose I'll go out again. There is something in me that says if a town is afraid of its children, then the town is dead. Vandals, you might remember, were able to ravage Rome because the empire was already decadent and defenseless.

I suppose Old Calvinist Oostburg is just a part of this nation's past, as much as today's Oostburg is part of this nation's future. Perhaps I'm expecting too much of a town with a fascinating history—my hometown. Perhaps Oostburg is a microcosm. Oostburg's problems are everyone's problems.

More sad than angry, I'll not sleep as well tonight in downtown Oostburg.

Bean-Walking

Waterweed is a hearty plant that shoots up and out like a green sky-rocket and mingles into the long rows of soybeans, gradually strangling the life out of plants which, to say the least, are more desirable. Dogbane is a thin, pointy cousin of the familiar milkweed; its roots burrow deep within the soil, sometimes too deep to be pulled out by the cultivator. Like its cousin the milkweed, dogbane grows on a lateral root that runs about six inches underground, and, sadly, does not die when the plant above the soil is picked or pulled out or hoed down.

To the farmer, those weeds are an eternal nemesis. In fact, I myself have thought that a healthy stand of milkweed, clogging the rows of soybeans, somehow signified all the clout of Adam's curse centered in my row of a particular section of Sioux County farmland.

Since most farmers rotate their crops, from corn to beans to corn to beans in successive years, "volunteer" corn can also tyrannize a bean field. It hides amid the rows in solitary stalks, or it blasts through the beans in a festival of green where an entire ear from last year's harvest has germinated in the topsoil. Unlike the dogbane and milkweed, volunteer corn jerks out completely in one hefty pull.

And then there is the button weed and wild sunflower and cocklebur, three stinkers whose size alone testifies to the power of sin. All three can grow up strong as tough old rose bushes—hearty, stubborn things, a sure pain in the back to the weed-puller. These resolute characters nearly always sprout in schools like fish, so the moment you see one you can bet your best pair of work gloves that there are more of them watching you from an adjacent row. Even worse, every bean-walker knows that after you think you have every last one of them, after you've looked over your shoulder one last time, somehow there are two or three still hiding among the beans, ready for that moment when you are safely out of sight, eager to burst through the beans like some smart bully.

This short manual in noxious weeds is being recited by an annual bean-walker—not a farmer but a teacher by profession, someone who finds bean-walking for his father-in-law something akin to an annual dental checkup, a kind of necessary evil. Some years the work goes rather well; the weather appears empathetic, the fields seem clean (the corn borer problem rather minor last year), and, for some reason, unknown even to modern agriculturists, the broadleaves seem to grant us a reprieve. Then there are the other years, years when the early July heat and humidity get thick as a wet blanket, when the rows gush forth in volunteer corn like some Oklahoma oil field, when the broadleaves scream out a challenge as we rumble down the gravel road in the old pickup.

Regardless of what kind of year it is, the job is terribly tedious. The days seem as long as the half-mile rows, the weeds seem to multiply as you stumble into them, the corn gets more and more stubborn, and by the end of the day your back becomes so weak that you start to feel as if the top of your body is balancing precariously on its base—like a pair of circus acrobats, head to head, one on top of the other. An educated fool like myself, long liberated from the rigors of physical labor, inspired throughout the year by the work of the mind alone, can find walking even a small 20-acre plot of soybeans about as inspiring as last Monday's reheated scalloped potatoes.

In fact, if it weren't for the conversation which my father-in-law and I carry on every summer, I doubt that I would lend a hand in the annual festivities. When we stop for coffee breaks, however, we talk about things—about the synod just completed, about problems in the church, about happenings at school, about energy, about the past, the war, early farming techniques, the old days—it makes the whole job almost worthwhile.

It was during one of our walks last week that I learned something amid the tight-roping bean plants, for we were talking about satisfaction, both of us agreeing that we were among the most fortunate people in the world because we enjoy what we do for our livings. Although our jobs are not the same, my father-in-law testified that his love for farming equaled my love for teaching. And so we nodded away at each other, sharing a lidful of water from a silver-gray thermos, agreeing that we were both really lucky that way.

Then we went back to work, pulling and tugging, sometimes down on our knees when the waterweed grew thicker than the beans, and we jerked out the sin until supper time—the end of the day. Before we dug into our pork roast, my father-in-law prayed, as is his custom. I remember just one line, I'm ashamed to say, for the air was full of the sharp smell of hot broccoli, fresh from the garden. He said, "Bless that all we do, we do to thy honor."

"Now hold on," I might have said if I had dared. How in the world can someone walk all day in a bean field, tugging away at worthless broadleaves, nearly breaking his back on volunteer corn, all the time sweating like a roofer, and then still say that he's doing such work to the glory of the Lord? It seemed to me that was stretching Calvinism a bit too far.

How on earth was I to believe that this milkweed stain on my hands was somehow related to the kingdom? Munching on a forkful of cole slaw, I remembered my father-in-law's final look over a cleaned and tidy twenty acres and began to grope toward an answer.

Maybe when my father-in-law looks up and down the cleaned rows of soybeans, he sees the beauty of God's creation well managed—subdued, in fact. Maybe when he hauls his beans to the elevator and the man at the co-op says he didn't find much refuse in the whole wagonful, my father-in-law feels he has accomplished his calling as well as he can. Maybe when he looks out on an unwalked field and sees sin, very physically screaming out its defiance, he knows that soon—despite the heat and frustration, the sore back, the tired feet and dirty hands, the worn gloves, and the problems with his trick knee—soon sin will be lying helpless in the rows, withered by the sun, yellowing between the redeemed beans. Maybe that's what he means. I'm not sure I know exactly, because I'm not a farmer.

I know one thing. When we talk about happiness and satisfaction with one's work, I know, after eighty-five acres of soybeans, that my father-in-law's prayer is directly related to his earlier confession that he is indeed happy in his job. I know too that the amount of happiness he feels is directly related to the extent that he understands his obligation to, his dependence on, his atonement in the Lord. Holy vocation is, by definition, happy vocation.

So bring on next year's waterweeds. I don't think I'll enjoy them any more than I ever have, and the corn could easily be worse next year, especially if we get some high winds at harvest time. Another year older, my father-in-law will be more tired by supper time, his knee sore and stiff. But, by supper time, the dogbane and the milkweed and the volunteer corn will again lie withering in the sun; the rows of beans will stand upright between them; and my father-in-law will once more ask a blessing on the work we have done to the glory of God.

Prairie Story Revisited

The Plain has moods like the sea. . .
The plain grows dark; like the sea
It holds no shelter.
                                        —Hamlin Garland

Local legend has it that when the county ran the gravel road straight west to the South Dakota border, one stubborn farmer refused to fell the monstrous cottonwood out front of his house, the one the engineers said threatened the new roadway. There he was, his arms cradling a shotgun, saying no, politely, to the men with the saws.

So today the tree stands there, a half-canopy of silver leaves leaning over the blacktop road to the state line. Maybe the tree is too dangerous, only a foot or two off the shoulder, but it's still there, thick and stubborn and almost mean, like the farmer who years ago fervently held his ground.

I had almost forgotten the story, but it returns to me now, after two years away from Iowa's prairie flatland. It returned to me when I returned to the plains, because the story's characters are the stock fare of old prairie life. The farmer with a shotgun—lean, shoulders stooped, lips chapped, face leathered—the kind of man who looks like the farmer in Grant Wood's famous painting, "American Gothic," but the kind of man who doesn't laugh at the painter's odd joke; and the tree—committed stubbornly to slow growth, tousled maybe by a northwest wind. And that looming third character, the prairie itself, today's immense garden of tall corn and beans; the plains flatland that farm wives called an ocean long before Hamlin Garland did, the sea of westward rolling hills beneath the hemisphere of broad horizon, the land so well drawn by Frederick Manfred, and before him, Rolvaag.

It is the prairie that really makes the farmer's story. It is the prairie sun that blotches the skin on his resolute face and the prairie wind twists the cottonwood's yearly growth. It is the land itself that firms their mutual stubbornness, that makes the farmer lock his jaw and look up to the cottonwood as some leafy alter ego, a symbol of his own capacity to endure during the ritual threats of mean prairie seasons—the heat of summer, the cold of winter, and always the scathing winds. Perhaps that farmer with the shotgun saw in the cottonwood a kindred spirit, a cohort, in the prairie epic.

Trees are no mere commodity here. Even today they are of immigrant stock, standing defiant on the sweep of flatland or pushed around by the gusty tempers of some very real Calvinist God. Even today, locked in the semi-security of air-conditioned tractor cabs equipped with the latest in corn pickers and bean harvesters, today's prairie farmer lives precariously in the hands of God, his crop and his family's livelihood determined, in a sense, by God's hand in nature—the length of the growing season, the path of summer hailstorms, the kindness of the wind.

Clinging ruggedly to the surface waters of the prairie ocean, folks here dig themselves into the earth—like the cottonwood—and live, sometimes too stubbornly perhaps, in the old ways, the ways that have let them live out here for a century. The prairie is no asphalt world, no super-domed existence. On the prairie, people live in the presence of a God who appears each season in the image of Old Testament Jehovah.

We've come back to northwest Iowa from the shelter of Wisconsin forests, where there is no straight-edge horizon; and the old man's story makes much more sense now that I can stand on the bare swell of a prairie hill and look over this broad land's patchwork. Here and there farm groves sit in huddled shadows against the plain.

Out here, exposed and vulnerable, folks can rest in God's favor. But when his disfavor slashes them with wind or flattens them with heat or hail, they wrestle it as physically as Jacob wrestled with God. There are no shadows here, no forests, no mountains to hide behind. The outfurled land nowhere offers relief. When some grand last trumpet sounds, no man will run to hide on the plains.

Last night a strong wind staggered the maples in front of our home. You could hear the startled leaves through the closed bedroom window, and I worried about our trees.

This morning I noticed that a neighbor had lost a branch from his front-yard elm. The tree looked like a spread compass, the snapped limb half-hanging to the ground. It hurt me to see it dangling there, its leaves already curling, because the image cut me to the very edge of life. It reminded me again of the old farmer standing out there with his cottonwood, shotgun in hand, saying no to some county engineer, as if it were he they were after with their saws. Because, in a prairie way, it was.

Real Estate

It used to be said that a man's house was his castle. Today, I am told, the average family picks up and moves every four years. In such a short time, the likelihood of a house becoming a real castle—or a home for that matter—seems rather unlikely.

It was not always that way. There was a time when people chose houses with the same scrutiny they used in finding spouses, sure that there was a similar kind of betrothal inherent in the process. The record of that kind of commitment is written on the farm homes on the back roads of every state and province of the continent.

If you get off the freeways you'll see them, two or three every mile—farm homes that changed shapes as frequently as the family grew or changed. There may be millions of them on the rural routes of the continent, but their shapes are as individual as fingerprints. In the Midwest they were probably constructed in perfectly rectangular shapes, maybe four basic rooms formed of thick masonry or locally-cut timber, or marbled with the stones lugged up from an adjacent field. There may be a small porch out front, its roof supported by two or three or four or more round columns, the exact number depending on either how much capital there was to build, or whether or not pa and ma took much stock in sitting out front on warm summer nights.

As the family and/or crops prospered, little *hoekjes* were hammered on like lean-tos—maybe a back entrance for overcoats and four-buckle boots, or maybe something more elaborate like the front room that ma always wanted. And things kept expanding like that—an enlargement of the dining room, the addition of indoor plumbing, or the enclosure of the front porch—until that original rectangle was nearly lost amid the cubicle additions, until the house, become home, turned into something of a museum exhibit, an American castle with a built-in historical record of its own inhabitants, a rather odd-shaped illustration of necessity and invention commingled.

Thousands of such homes line the inside roads of rural areas and the streets of towns and cities today, a century of grandpas and grandmas later. The awkward sprawling things seem to resemble those little interlocking wooden puzzles you can buy for a dollar or two, the kind that once apart seem a lifelong headache to reconstruct.

We miss that kind of real estate if we stick to the freeways, of course, for those concrete miracles make it easy for us to pass by the everyday lives of farmers and village merchants from Arkansas to Alberta. Freeways keep us on a production line of foil-wrapped hamburgers that all taste the same, motel rooms that all look the same, and, of course, Coca-Cola. If freeways are like jet travel, the back roads are bus routes. Take the back roads and you can't help smelling manure and skunk, or slowing down for tractors and trucks, or here and there noticing an old orange and black A & W drive-in with a gravel parking lot, something off the cover of a *Saturday Evening Post.* Take the back roads and you'll see real houses, man's natural habitat.

City houses tell their stories too. Every city has its own "heritage hills"; not to drive past the opulent splendor of Victorian gimmickry is to miss a great free trip through the gilded monuments of time. I'm told that nearly a century ago lumber barons in Waupun, Wisconsin, staged a one-upmanship struggle in fanciness, designing real frame and brick castles, one after another, that still line the streets of that town. Each of the mansions has peaks and gables festooned with intricate, ornamental carvings, a pinnacled turret or two at the corners, joined by long porches with a hundred or more hand-carved wood spokes that circle the

whole monstrosity. They stand there amid the elms like testimonies to painstaking workmanship now almost extinct; but they trumpet human pride just as clearly. Their haunting exteriors are matched only by their elaborate oak interiors. They portray an era which will not come again.

Our houses are our signatures in a way, just as all of our actions illustrate or explain something of who we are and what are our dreams. From the clapboard shacks of the Mississippi Delta tenant farmers, to the modern split-levels of today's suburban living, to the almost volcanic-looking earth homes erupting out of the ground, we explain ourselves—our plight or our silly pretentiousness—by our visions of what has long been the American dream of home-ownership. Often, however, our homes can be misunderstood as easily as we can misunderstand the homes of others.

It wasn't Solomon who wrote that cleanliness was next to Godliness. We might remember that as we admire the razor-cut lawns and floral regalia of our Orange Citys and Lyndens. Today there is as much trouble in the ranch villas of our clean-cut bedroom communities as there is in the dilapidated public housing of the inner cities; the latest in a long line of American assassins lived in the richest suburb of Denver.

Finally, I suppose, we can't read salvation or even accomplishment in the straight lines of new shingles or the length of wrought-iron fence, or even the number of geraniums sprouting from window boxes. The measure of a good house is taken in its ability to become a real home, and the arrangements of bric-a-brac, the number or shape of evergreen sentries at the front step, the aluminum siding or the clean white paint job, the thick bed of tulips, the new fireplace or cedar porch—none of it amounts to a hill of beans if the house, like each of us, won't respond to its calling.

Our signatures are no more credible than our souls. Our houses may illustrate our familial sagas, they may testify to our slavish materialism or our penury, but they'll not do much more.

Unless the warmth of home abides within our walls—

whether they be slate or dry-wall—our houses will be little more than what psychologists call our "environments."

And they'll not save us or our kids.

Thirty-five and Counting

Losing hair is bad enough, but growing old carries with it a whole bargain shelf full of bonus humiliations, especially for those who have not taken the time to note that their own evening yawns occur earlier with every passing year. Some of us don't believe the sermons of gimpy knees or aching feet. Some just refuse to listen. But age is there in silver hair around the temples, in sagging jowls, and in medicine cabinets that seem always too full.

Forgetfulness, some say, is a bonus of the aging process. Sometimes we come out of church and stand there for one humiliating minute, scanning the parking lot, realizing we haven't the slightest idea where we parked the station wagon barely an hour before.

We see age in our hands, in the thin, almost brittle skin and the network of wiry chicken tracks over the surface, here and there a bothersome brown blotch, so much more embarrassing than even our own kid's dirty fingernails. Age does it.

Subtly, age adjusts our views, curbs our enthusiasms, and changes the way we look at most everything—the way we look at adolescence, for example. Fifteen-year-old kids in roving bands, hanging out downtown or pulling wheelies on their mopeds, start to look scary, like some awful malignancy in the culture at large, a frightful symbol of decadence. Sometimes age makes us hardnosed.

But lately I've come to think that none of those physical or emotional changes the years slowly cure within us are as trying as an associated phenomenon: when we reach thirty-five, we attend more funerals than we ever have before. They come with more frequency, and inevitably they rob us of intimacy we might have thought we could never lose. When we are thirty-five, death begins to steal away the mighty standards of our lives—our uncles and aunts, our mothers and fathers, and our older friends, those we assumed to be permanent players in the drama of our own lives. But suddenly, they're gone. And we go off again to the funeral. More than anything else, perhaps it's death we fear in growing older.

Recently we went—my wife and I—first to the wake and the next day to the funeral. And it's difficult for thirty-five-year-old novices, because standing before an open casket is no occasion for small talk. Really, there are no words, so you shake hands slowly and try to coax your eyes and mouth into some visage of sympathy, some half-smile, half-frown that tells the grieving you think you know how they must feel.

I'm not sure the wife of the deceased even knew me when I greeted her. Her eyes were swimming in grief, and the resolution on her lips and in her face seemed trancelike; if stoic, then artificially so. And I felt myself an intruder into her sorrow, one of dozens, maybe hundreds, who would file by her and the grim semicircle of family, in machine-like precision, all of us wearing the same half-smile, half-frown, all of us as tongue-tied, all of us meaning well, but all of us passengers aboard the same time-bound ritual of the funeral tradition. Mostly, I felt sorry for her, because of her husband and because of the long column of well-wishers lining up behind me that by sheer numbers alone, her eyes told me, would turn the true expressions of sympathy into some overtaxing, emotional gauntlet. When we left, I feared for that woman.

My wife said we had one more call to make, the mother of the deceased. It wasn't my idea; I had already seen enough.

When we arrived, the elderly woman apologized for not setting coffee; then she sat in her rocker, over her shoulder on a paneled wall, a flag-sized frame full of ovals, wedding pictures, everyone from her own parents back in the old country to those of her six children, a register of joy in three rows spread over something close to sixty years of marital bliss on two continents. But this son was the third of her boys to go, and none of them had lived to sixty. Most of the ovals were only memories.

She rocked very slowly, moving only with a slight tilt of her head, in and out, but that eighty-year-old woman did most of the talking. "I think he looked so good," she said. "Didn't you?"

My wife agreed.

"And it was so quick. And there was no suffering too. Ja, that's something, isn't it?" She jerked her skirt over her knees. "And so how has it been for you folks?"

To me, it was clear when we left that the elderly woman had taken the death of her third son in more even stride than any of us, even myself—half her age and unaccustomed to funerals.

William Hazlitt once started an essay with this line: "No young man thinks that he shall ever die." But it took an eighty-year-old woman who had already seen two of her sons buried to explicate it for me. Hazlitt is right, of course, because he speaks of the young and not of the old.

It is one of the small advantages of growing older, perhaps—amid the anguish of thinning hair, of drying skin, of humiliating forgetfulness—that we inch ever closer to the end. And the closer we come, the easier it may be to accept. Death's trauma eases when our compliance with ultimate destiny becomes a matter of fact. Our Lord simply draws nearer.

This much I learned at thirty-five.

Electric Socks and the Incarnation

Now I don't want to sound like some kind of Siouxland Scrooge, but it seems to me that every year Christmas brings the same kind of problems around. The first Saturday night in December, my wife and I look at each other with the same appraising look, and try to come up with some kind of idea for each other's Christmas present. After all, the tradition of giving presents is far too deeply entrenched within us to forego lightly. But the problem is always the same: what can we possibly buy for each other—we seem to have everything. What gift will satisfy the romantic spirit of opening presents around a tree—that is, something both delightful and practical.

So, we say, what do we really want? My wife says a dishwasher; I say a new economy car. Well, neither of those ideas are really any help, so we keep thinking. I ask myself what is it she really needs? Ah, hah—a remodeled bathroom. Well, how romantic is a remodeled bathroom? Besides, I don't know how to begin to wrap up a toilet bowl or a new sink. And how do you put a remodeling job under a five-foot spruce? I tell myself it's out of the question anyway—things like that take time and discussion, maybe even a good argument or two. I couldn't just surprise her early on Christmas morning by ripping out a bathtub. Be realistic, I tell myself.

The TV offers a fine array of Christmas gifts. Did you ever notice how the goods advertised change with the season? Suddenly, maybe a day or two after the smell of turkey is out of your nostrils, all kinds of new gift ideas jump off the screen, each of them unbelievably practical—so practical you find yourself wondering how on earth any household could possibly ever have functioned without them. This year's top attraction is a food machine of sorts—an elaborate gizmo, complete with thirty-seven detachable accessories, that sits on a kitchen counter and does most everything but slaughter the cattle. Another favorite is a Presto donut cooker—no real home should be without it—just drop in a little dough, plug the thing in, listen to it sizzle, and whammo: two plump donuts drop to the countertop. Goodbye, *ole bollen.*

Gloves is another item rarely advertised except at Christmas. Ever notice how fancy gloves are made today—racing stripes, virgin wool, or Korean calf-skin— just perfect for touring meandering Italian highways in your Ferrari. Come to think of it, my wife's gloves do look rather proletarian. Or a new watch, one with a lighted dial that records the number of laps you run around the gym even if you don't jog—a real digital delight.

Well, I still don't know what to get her, and the TV is no help at all. Then, just as I'm about to give up and buy some boring old gift certificate, a cute little catalogue arrives in the mail, as if somebody out there was really thinking about me and my problems. In fact, the crazy thing even has my name on it. "Here it is," it announces in bold-face type, "an important message for Mr. Schaat" (the name is always spelled wrong), and your Christmas catalogue from "Foster House Bonanza of Gifts." You know the type—a little five-by-eight rag chocked full of your crazy uncle's inventive failures. So I page through it, spirits rising. But no, she doesn't need a five-foot inflatable Santa Claus you can put anywhere in the home; or electric socks; or paisley long underwear in a matching set, perfect for the cold Iowa nights; or a multi-purpose jackknife from Norway, efficiently equipped with eleven different blades capable of performing more than 300 common household tasks.

Obviously, the bonanza is a blow-out. Now it's the middle of December. Still no gift in sight, and those gift certificates really start looking more and more attractive.

Well, all of this sets me to thinking about needs and wants. And, good old Calvinist that I am, I am reminded that what I want may not be what I need, and how what she needs may not be what she wants, and how we sometimes easily confuse what we want with what we need, and how our entire society has so many wants and so few needs, at least needs that can be bought in your local K-Mart. So, like Hamlet the Prince, I keep thinking, since it's much easier than buying.

But some of that thinking is rather painful; for instance, the only kinds of needs we have as a family, the only kinds of needs I have as an individual, that we all have as a culture, that we have as creatures of our Lord, are those needs which absolutely cannot be satisfied by catalogues which feature five-foot inflatable Santas, perfect for any room of the home. You can't put fancy gloves on those needs. You can't put fancy watches on the wrists of those needs. Those needs would have no use for a remodeled bathroom.

In fact, those needs are met only through one gift, a gift far more expensive than a new dishwasher or economy car. Those needs have already been met by a gift, a gift which has set a pattern for all giving we do this season, and a pattern which we have dropped in favor of snowmobiles, mopeds, Star War toys, dolls that snuggle, and Musk aftershave, all neatly wrapped in reusable bows.

God's gift, a Son to die for our sins, has satisfied all of our needs—but apparently not all our wants, not even for us Christians. Our wants go raging on unsatisfied, like a monster we have created ourselves, a Frankenstein which threatens to make us the richest poor people in the history of civilization. I guess we must face the fact that we live in a culture which has lost the valued distinction between *wants* and *needs*, and that we Christians have to see that our culture has affected us to such an extent that we too, we Christians, have forgotten that all our *needs*, our real *needs*, our eternal *needs*, our *needs* for this world and the next, have been forever satisfied with the Incarnation, for if the Lord is my shepherd, I shall not want.

But there's more to it. Even though His gift satisfied all

our needs, it may in fact be most unwanted at Christmas. After all, at this season of the year, who among us really takes George Beverly Shea seriously when he sings, "I'd rather have Jesus than silver or gold?" Oh, it's a nice line, we say, nodding our heads, and maybe, if the words are appropriately mounted on a nice bronze background, the plaque might even make a decent gift for someone's grand-mother.

The fact is that Christ's birth and death and what it means for us as Christians may be least important for us at Christmas, because our wants become so exaggerated, so inflated, so glorious, that our *needs*, that which the Incarnation gave freely to us, become lost, forgotten amid the five-foot inflatable Santas.

So tomorrow is Christmas, and I'm not going to tell you what I bought my wife because it's going to be a secret. And I don't know if my gift is an attempt to follow our Father's example in giving either. For all my thinking about Christmas and giving at Christmas and wants and needs and gloves and remodeled bathrooms, I know I'm still woefully short of coming up to the standards set so long ago at Bethlehem.

The only thing I know for sure is that His gift excuses all my stumbling and all my "noble" failures. Even if my wife's gift fails to light up her eyes, I know His gift has given us both all the light and life we'll ever need.

Walking Billboards

I saw her in K-Mart, probably sixty years old, grand-motherly plump, her hair done up just that morning. She looked perfectly loving—the kind of woman whose chewy chocolate chip cookies taste the way cookies are supposed to taste, whose kitchen is an assortment of delights.

But around her, over her farm wife's shoulders, she wore a bright yellow plastic jacket, big as a pup tent, and on her back, in lurid green and fancy script, just two words— "Seamless Gutters."

Today people say we live in a world where there are no rights or wrongs, so who am I to condemn this woman's aesthetic sensibility?

Certainly it isn't illegal for her to be a walking advertise-ment for her husband's business. No one would lock her up for it. But, somehow, to my tastes, her "Seamless Gutters" fit snugly under a slightly elitist term fully as dangerous to use as it is useful to apply. To me, her choice of apparel seemed tacky.

So I ask myself, what on earth would prompt such a woman to become a billboard for her husband's specialty company, to act as if she were some unemployed Texas pompom girl? Why—when she could have chosen a shawl or a nice cable-knit cardigan—why does she deck herself in green and yellow hype?

There has to be an explanation. Maybe all one has to do is wander into any sports store and check the price tags on the Adidas T-shirts. They are not free, after all. People— regular people, intelligent people, even upper class folk—

pay out their hard-earned money to advertise most anything, from taverns to muffler shops, from Chevy pickups to a half-pound rubber running shoe with a fancy design on the shank.

It is not only the cult jogger or the car fancier. Everybody is doing it. Women—and men—gladly pay exorbitant prices for jeans with some fancy name burned or stitched on the bottoms. It is as if they wanted to be identified as belonging to their designer's herd.

Maybe Grandma Seamless Gutters, like the rest of us, pulled on her yellow gear not by choice but by fad—that mad cultural emotion by which people proclaim their individuality by conforming to whatever is hip. Company jackets, designer jeans and lettered T-shirts are the rage today, and few of us—not even grandmothers—can escape the commands of a fad.

But even a fad has a cause. A fad is a fashion, and no fashion can grow where people aren't willing to nurture it. Why is it that we have become so completely subservient to business interests that we are willing to don their advertising, willing to pay to become walking billboards adorned in bright blues and greens?

Sociologists probably could explain it. They probably would tell you the family is the cause. As the family bond continues to deteriorate in contemporary society, we look to other groups for the identity family once provided.

For many of us, ethnicity disappears when family names become obsolete. In chance meetings with people today, few of us even bother with last names: each of us is simply Sid or Joan or Bob, as if there were no other Bobs between here and the state line.

When family names have lost their usefulness, we seek identity by our employment—Bill's Plumbing and Heating, or our favorite voluntary organization, Lake Milton Fire Department, or our neighborhood tavern, Fred and Emma's Package Goods. Whatever we choose, we slap it on our backs like numbers pinned to the backs of rodeo ropers so the crowd can see where we belong in the Yellow Pages.

We might blame the fad on the Puritan ethic, the sense

of calling that we've inherited from the Reformation, from practical Yankees like Ben Franklin, from our own American dreams of a good job and a good house in the suburbs.

Work is righteous to many of us; why not make a habit of our employment? By their work ye shall know them. Grandma Seamless Gutters wanted everyone in K-Mart to know that she and her husband were no low-down welfare cheaters.

We might blame our consumer society. Nearly half of *Time* magazine is advertising copy today, and the newspaper ratio is worse. We all know that perhaps the most creative work on TV is done on the commercials.

In June the world of advertising probably will call more of our college graduates than the field of social work, so why shouldn't the rest of us—the blue collars, the government workers, the execs, the housewives and househusbands—get in on the action?

Besides, wearing company jackets and advertising T-shirts is something of a power show. Advertising dupes people—at least everybody else. By wearing the ads, we muscle our way through its seductive power and lay convincing claim to our own invulnerability.

It is more than just family we're buying into. Things like designer jeans and the complete Nike outfit—hooded sweatshirt, pants, and shoes—become 100 percent creeds, really. Today, when you say Nike, you've said it all about yourself. A clerical collar illustrates one's values no more clearly.

And all the while Adidas shoes and Arctic Cats and countless radio stations and your uncle's excavation crew trucks away the rewards from free advertisement.

It used to be that the diner down the block had to hire a transient to stick his head through the old sandwich boards and stand on the sidewalk with the daily special plate-lunch chalked on his chest. Today people pay for the honor. The best and the brightest, the most fit, the ones with the best legs—we're all walking billboards.

Yet, somehow, Grandma's Seamless Gutters jacket seems tacky to me, just plain tacky.

Anyway, my wife and I are going to a movie tonight, and I've got to find my sweater—you know, the striped one I got on sale last spring, the one with the little alligator.

Kidney Stone

Pastor Beamon took the call about 8:30 a.m., on Monday, and Mondays are sometimes a preacher's worst day, as we all know. Jeanne Sigenthaler's call pulled him away from the TV, where he was watching some morning show interview of a city councilman who was trying to excite viewers about a volunteer, city-wide, clean-up project. Pastor Beamon hadn't had his coffee. Jeanne told him how her brother (only 25 or so, she said, if you can believe it) had been taken in to emergency during the night for a kidney stone. Pain nearly tore him apart, she said, and would he start up the prayer chain for Paul's insides—not to mention his own soul, should something unthinkable occur?

First he got his coffee, then he slipped out the list from the drawer beneath the phone. Mondays make him growly sometimes, because likely as not the sermon didn't sail like it had when he'd preached it in his mind. So he called Mrs. Lennox and told her how Jeanne Sigenthaler's brother Paul had a kidney stone that was giving him a great deal of pain, and how she should send the news along the prayer chain. Mrs. Lennox thought twenty-five was terribly young for a stone, and Pastor Beamon said maybe that wasn't what it was, because this boy Paul was just in at the hospital this morning and maybe the doctors would call it something else once they put him through some tests; but whatever it was, the kid sure had pain.

When Mrs. Lennox called Sadie Vedema, she said first of all how this was a prayer chain call; she didn't want Sadie

109

thinking it was anything other than business, not after what Sadie said about people in their church at the last Bible study. "Honestly, people would just stare at you if you'd carry your own Bible into church," she had said. Mrs. Lennox hated such vague generalizations—"Who?" she had said to Sadie right there over fresh banana bread, "Alma Draayers? Bill Royster? Ann—my own sister, Ann?" Sadie just sat there fuming with her finger pointing at some red print in the New Testament. So Mrs. Lennox didn't want her thinking the call was personal. She told Sadie that Jeanne Sigenthaler's brother (whom she didn't know personally and she didn't think went to their church at all) was having some tests on what he thought was a kidney stone, but whatever it was gave him more than a little pain, and it was something all right because the boy was so young—not even thirty yet. Sadie said she didn't know that Jeanne had a brother that age.

Sadie had the prayer list written down on the blank week behind the month of January in the calendar she got from the church Board of Missions. She called the Rozemas, but Julie wasn't home, which was okay because she thought her husband, Mark, was such a gentleman anyway, and she never really got a chance to talk to a man with a master's degree. She told Mark that Jeanne Sigenthaler's brother was having tests that day in the hospital for some rough pain he'd been having, and that they were thinking maybe it was kidney stones, but he seemed (she couldn't remember his name) so young to be bothered by stones like that, and what on earth would happen to a person who already had such ailments once he got to her own age? Mark Rozema told her she could be sure it would be passed along and he thanked her kindly for the call and her concern. He had such a gift of speech, she thought, and his hair always looked so right, even if it was a bit unkempt. Julie cut his hair—she was sure.

Mark Rozema was tired of being out-of-work and tired of walking their little girl to the park, as if he was just another young mother with a kid constantly teething. He wasn't about to be a part of a prayer chain, so he wrote it down on a piece of pink notepaper that said "While You

Were Out" over the top of the page, and he figured Julie would take care of it when she came home from Dr. Blakely's for lunch, the lunch he was tired of cooking up day-after-day while his wife supported both the baby and him. Just before one o'clock Julie told Mrs. Edwards that Mark had taken the call and she wasn't so sure of the details, but Jeanne Sigenthaler's brother had been taken in to the hospital for severe pain he had been suffering, and because he was so young the doctors were going to give him a real battery of tests to be sure they got a handle on whatever it was that bothered him. Ann Edwards asked Julie what she thought, since Julie had, after all, taken some medical training, and Julie said it would be impossible to guess what it could be, but in someone that young, it could be nothing more than gas, but whatever it was, she told Ann to be praying for the entire family because emergencies were frequently the best opportunities to bring people together and help them over their personal problems. She looked over at her husband when she said it, but he didn't look up from draining the hamburger grease into an old butter tub.

Mrs. Edwards tipped up the iron after finishing her husband's shirt and called Harold Jensen. She told Harold that Jeanne Sigenthaler's family was having some problems, maybe even something of a religious crisis, because of Jeanne's younger brother's being suddenly taken to the hospital with a mysterious illness—full of pain, she said, but Julie Rozema thought it could have been simply gas, but that it would be just like the Lord to bring people together that way, almost fool them into thinking deeply about spiritual things. Another one of His mysterious ways, she said. But you can imagine what such a thing would do to the boy's mother.

Harold Jensen pulled a card from his wallet and dialed "spiritual crisis" on the outer wheel. The hole in the middle pointed at some Bible passages, so he looked one up before he called Margaret Symonds. Ever since his father's death, Harold had found that card a blessing. He told Margaret there were two passages in Hebrews he could suggest for meditation, and he argued that if all of them had more

111

Bible knowledge they could move through their personal Gethsemanes with less pain. (He remembered hearing a preacher in Ft. Lauderdale talk about "personal Gethsemanes.") Finally, he remembered to tell her about Jeanne Sigenthaler's mother's problems, and how it was up to each of them on the prayer chain to just sit right down and pray for the woman, because, hey, it could happen to any of them.

Margaret Symonds was the last link. She whispered a short prayer immediately, and then, over her boiled baloney, went through the request in more detail before supper, because she believed, as we all do, in the power of prayer.

Jeanne Sigenthaler called Pastor Beamon just before the late news, and she told him how her brother had passed the stone before surgery. She told him how the nurse told her brother to use the restroom if he could, and how he went into that little room and how he just passed it, right then and there, and how it was almost like a miracle.

Pastor Beamon agreed it was and said how we often don't call things like that miracles when, in fact, we should. Jeanne said how he was right, and how it came from the prayer chain for sure, and how she could feel it like an electric current the whole time she was there with her brother in the hospital. Be sure to tell them, will you?—be sure to call it in how all of it turned out right.

Pastor Beamon figured he'd put it off for the night, because it would be such a bother after ten, and besides it would be good to announce a miracle come Sunday morning.

And, oh yes, Jeanne said, one more thing—how her mother was there too and how even she thought it was a miracle the way her son just kicked out that stone without having to go under the knife. From my mother that's something, Jeanne said, considering that she hadn't been to church for years already. That's really something, she said.

Pastor Beamon prayed for Jeanne's mother too yet that night.

Prophet With A Cane

O my people, hear my teaching;
listen to the words of my mouth.
I will open my mouth in parables,
I will utter things hidden from of old—
things, our fathers have told us.

Psalm 78:1-3

Wilma walks with an odd aluminum cane, with a clear plastic handle grip like a tricycle's and a four-pronged base—for stability, I suppose. She doesn't walk well. She's old now, and she's heavy, too heavy—she's always been too heavy, even years ago when her husband was alive. It's a major undertaking for her to come through our front door—left foot up, then the cane, then right foot—the door slipping shut as her body leans through the threshhold.

Maybe that's why her occasional visits sometimes linger a half-hour or so beyond what we call "long enough." Maybe once she's in the door, it's just too difficult for her to think so quickly about leaving, about pulling herself up again from the lightweight kitchen chair she threatens. So she sits there as if simply getting in through the door was accomplishment enough to merit an audience.

But I'm old enough to know there is another reason that when she comes in, it's always to sit. She's alone now, sitting at night at her kitchen table, smoking. No one is supposed to know about the cigarettes. I think it's a menthol brand, those long ones. At night when I come back

113

downstairs from putting the kids to bed, I see her smoking. Her kitchen window, hung with half-curtains, is no more than twenty feet from the window at the top of our stairs. The cigarette is tucked into an ash tray, a thin line of smoke rising a foot high maybe, razor-straight, until it pours into curls. Every night, solitaire. Wilma is alone, and I see her there at her kitchen table, nightly dealing out another hand of solitaire. Her kids are all grown and moved away from town; one daughter comes over on Saturday afternoons to help clean for Sunday.

Today is Saturday. This afternoon she lumbered through our front door and came to rest on the kitchen chair, one hand slumped over the cane's handle grip. She bumped into the relaxed freedom of my Saturday afternoon, and I don't remember anymore how she started talking. A decade of late-night solitaire makes you a hair-trigger talker, I suppose.

I stood while she sat; I wanted her to know I was busy—reading the newspaper, something about Central America. That afternoon her grandson, she said, stayed in the house while his mother cleaned up the place for her. That was it. That's what started her talking—the street and car accidents.

Wilma said she was scared of kids and cars. She had been scared for fifty years, ever since the day she was babysitting little Nellie—you know, Mrs. Swanson. . . she used to be your neighbor?—ever since little Nellie jerked her little hand away and tore into Main Street—right in front of the grocery store downtown—where Evelyn Brasser hit her with her Chevy. Little Nellie, just three-and-a-half years old. And Evelyn was just coming from high school. Bang! Right downtown.

Wilma's story was new to me; already a half-century old, but to me it was new. I sat down across the table from her.

She said Marv Gustafson took little Nellie in his arms, picked her up right off the cement and carried her to Doc Mand's house—that's the one Fred and Alice live in now, just south of the new bank building. But the doctor was gone out somewhere to a farm where there was no phone.

114

So some men drove out to get him right away, and when he came back he examined her for broken bones and such and says it looks to him like she's okay. But watch her close, he says to me. I was just seventeen—what did I know? And little Nellie's mother, that's Alma, is in the hospital for gall bladder surgery—and that's no picnic either, I can tell you. So later that night little Nellie starts to vomit, and my mother says it's nothing to be worrying about. "Vomiting is really nothing at all," she said—Ma did.

Doc Mand stopped in later, right before bed. When I told him little Nellie had vomited, he just stared for a minute. "Wrap her up in a blanket," he said, "she's going this minute to the hospital." My lands! I was seventeen. And already I felt so terrible—like all of it was my fault. Nellie just jerked her hand out of mine and ran into the street—what could I do? And this Evelyn Brasser—you know? the woman that hit her?—she felt just awful about it. And it wasn't her fault either.

Three days we waited to see if little Nellie would live or die. The doctors said she had a tiny fracture right here over her nose, and if it was broken completely, she would likely die—if it was only a crack she'd get over it completely. When you're young you know how fast things heal. And all the time her own mother's lying there recovering from gall bladder surgery. Doc Mand said Alma shouldn't know about her only child hanging there between life and death. So little Nellie's father would go up to visit his daughter for awhile and then visit his wife, being sure to pull his coat on before he came to his wife's room—just to make sure it looked like he'd just come in from the outside.

And you can imagine what it was for me—three days of waiting for death—and I was just seventeen years old, and I felt so responsible.

Wilma's eyes glistened in the searing memory of guilt. She turned away. I put my elbows up on the table. But little Nellie lived, I know. Thirty years later I grew up with little Nellie's oldest son. So I guessed her story was over—this story.

"Twenty-five years later, to the month, twenty-five years later, my son Eddie had that awful accident on the motorcycle," she tells me. When she says it, the images come back to me because this one I remember. I was a little boy when it happened, but I remember my father praying about Eddie over our supper—"be with Eddie and his mother and father, and be with the rest of the family"— and I remember the preacher praying. Three weeks, Wilma's boy, just seventeen, hit by a drunk driver, suspended between life and death—like little Nellie—and a whole village watched and prayed again.

And there was a girl killed on Eddie's motorcycle that Sunday afternoon. She was the only daughter of Evelyn Brasser, Wilma tells me, the same Evelyn Brasser that twenty-five years before had hit little Nellie right there in front of the grocery store on Main Street. I didn't go to the girl's funeral, Wilma says, because it was life or death with Eddie the whole time. So I never talked to Evelyn Brasser after that horrible accident, she says.

And five years later, a year or two after my husband died, I got a job at the shoe factory. The first day I came there, Evelyn—she worked there for years already— Evelyn sees me on the sidewalk, walking up. And she marches directly to the boss. "I won't have that woman working here," she tells the boss. "I won't have it," she says. And he says he couldn't refuse me work for that reason. So right then and there Evelyn quit rather than work with me. She quit right there on the first morning I came up to work —because of me.

My lands, I felt terrible. But what could I do? My kids had to eat. Should I just have to quit because Evelyn Brasser won't talk to me? I couldn't.

She comes back to work a week later maybe. I don't know why. And the supervisor puts us together—"show Wilma how to sew these shanks," he says to Evelyn. So he made her talk to me. She had to talk to me.

And there we sat at that machine. "Evelyn," I says, "you can't hold this against me anymore. It wasn't me that did it. It wasn't even my own son. It was that drunk driver— he was responsible. You can't hold it against me anymore,"

I says.

"But my daughter is gone," she says. "And you still have your Eddie."

"Evelyn," I says, "the Lord has His plan for these things. I don't know why He made me sit at Eddie's bed for so long and wait for death. I don't know why Eddie lived. I don't know why your daughter died. But I know yet that our God has a plan in these things. And you know that too," I says, "and you can't hold it against me anymore—you can't."

And that was all it took. We started talking. That was it. All of that I can still remember so good.

Wilma pulled herself up on the odd-looking cane and opened the front door before taking a step. Her story was over.

"Stop in again, Wilma," I said. "I mean it."

A quarter hour, maybe, it took for her to walk next door. And probably she pulled a menthol cigarette from the black pouch she hides them in. And tonight when I bring the kids to bed, I'll likely see her there again, both elbows spread over her kitchen table, her eyes sweeping over red jacks and black kings, as her old hands flip up cards in groups of three.

And tomorrow I'll see her in church again, sitting down through the hymns like she always does, her cane parked up next to her in the pew.

Today Wilma took thirty minutes of my Saturday afternoon to spell out a biography of anguish and trust and patience, all wrapped in a testimony as real as blood and tears and the rhythmic beating of the human heart.

And this is just to say thanks, Wilma, for imposing.

Right and Wrong

Pardon me for talking about other people's kids, but this story you've got to hear. Two kids are talking about profound things like God and heaven above. The older one—let's call him Jeremy—is a kindergartener; he's the authority.

The younger one cocks his head. "When you die, do you get to be an angel?" he asks.

Jeremy wrinkles his nose. "Don't know," he says. "But in heaven you get everything you want—except guns."

Jeremy's claims tells us something about his parents. It's clear that they dislike seeing guns in Jeremy's hands—pop guns, cap guns, cork guns, even those fat rubber ones you squeeze little puff balls out of, the kind of bullets that even at close range feel like a kiss against your cheek. Mom and Dad, likely as not, keep guns away from Jeremy. "Guns don't make nice toys," they tell him, their eyebrows dipped menacingly.

But most parents know that some wars can't be won. Swipe a toy gun from a little boy and he'll use his pointer finger or pick up a tree branch that magically becomes a rifle. Jeremy's parents have tried to make guns horrid and sinful instruments of death, but even a kid owns his own imagination.

Jeremy's vision of heaven illustrates his own fascination with the contraband arms his parents despise. Everything you want is there in heaven, he says—except guns. Guns, he thinks, are beyond the reach of God's grace, even if they aren't beyond the range of his own desire. Like 'em or not,

119

guns are wrong.

The lines Jeremy has drawn between good and evil are clear, clearer than our own distinctions sometimes. To Reformed Christians who view this world as somehow "redeemable," Jeremy's doctrine may be heretical—kindergarten heresy, we might call it. Some Reformed Christians would say that guns themselves are not sinful. What we need, they might claim, is to redeem guns. Of course, Jeremy wouldn't understand that. Many of us don't.

But Jeremy's sentiment reminds us of one difficult job we face as parents and teachers: the task of discriminating between what is right and what is wrong, between carrom boards and video games, between Rook and five-card stud, between bingo and big-time betting, between TV movies and R-rated films—in short, between what's okay for our kids (and even ourselves), and what isn't. What's worse, it's a job that not so many years ago—when all movies were wrong—was easier, maybe, than it is today.

At the very beginning of this year, a freshman student I know—we'll call her Jill—attended a movie shown on the campus of the college where I teach, a college that calls itself a Christian college. The movie followed the lives of a group of married couples whose mutual friendship was interrupted when one of the husbands deserted his wife for a young lover. As movies go today, this one was rather "tame" really—some questionable lines and scenes, but no exploitation or deliberate manipulation, and very few jiggles.

She came to my office later. "I'm really surprised that they showed that movie here," she said. "I just didn't expect it." Quite frankly, Jill was disappointed. She might have said, "I thought this was a Christian college." That's what she meant.

Oddly enough, she had seen the movie before, in a regular theater—the kind her grandparents wouldn't have attended, even though the movies of their age were much less offensive. Apparently, seeing the movie in a theater was okay; seeing it on the campus of a Christian college implied, in her mind, a kind of institutional acceptance of everything on the screen—even the crude jokes about sex.

The lines she had drawn to define what was of Christ and what was of the Devil were erased, at least temporarily, by seeing the film on our campus. She was confused. Munching her popcorn in a theater somewhere, she might have seen the film as entertainment. Seated in the college chapel, she thought the film suddenly evil, too much a part of the sinful world she thought she would be sheltered from at a college that called itself Christian. She expected, I suppose, Walt Disney and nothing more.

At five years old, Jeremy has his values down pat: in heaven you get everything you want, except guns. Guns are naughty—that much he knows. Jill thought she had her values down too, until she saw a film she judged as sinfully beyond the limits of what a Christian college should show —regardless of whether or not she had seen it before.

Had we—administration, film council, teachers—erred in making her question her own sense of right and wrong? Did the college itself see its mandate as the destruction of the values with which Jill and others like her had come to school?

Pardon me for telling one more story, but somehow I think it fits. Not long ago I accompanied some students to a lecture by a famous author. I knew her only by her fiction, and I admired her for her compassion, for her ability to admit us intimately into the characters that stepped out of her pages, characters most readers grew to love.

She chose not to use the podium, sitting instead on the stage at the front. "I'm either seventy-two or seventy-three," she said, her thick silver hair pulled back from her forehead, her eyes, bright and intense, like her voice. For more than an hour she answered questions from two hundred people in a lecture hall, quietly, sincerely, emotionally. She was everything I would have wanted her to be; she was lovely in her regard for the young people she was addressing, passionate in commitment to writing, proud and strong in her convictions. I've seen enough writers who swagger like Hemingway; this one, I thought, would have made a grand grandmother.

One of our students asked her about her religious views.

"I've never been asked that question before," she said, and for a moment she looked almost uneasy. But then she explained how her Russian immigrant parents had sworn off faith in God after a lifetime of religious bigotry in the country they had left to come to America. This woman, so sweet and compassionate, so loving and grandmotherly, told us, openly and sincerely, that she was an avowed atheist.

I think my students were shocked; I know I was. The woman was an atheist, a radical feminist, even something of a socialist—and yet, despite all the ugliness we ordinarily associate with those tags, she glowed with a radiant love and concern for her fellowman. She broke through the distinctions we had set in our minds, distinctions maintaining that only Christians could love deeply and that atheists have no regard for anyone but themselves.

Then something strange happened. The moment her speech was concluded, she left the stage, walked directly to the student who had asked the question, then hugged and kissed her. And there I stood, thinking that my students would never be quite the same.

All of this is terribly dangerous, of course. Some of us would say that the Jill the moviegoer was right about that film—there is no place for movies like that on a Christian college campus. Some of us might say that atheism, socialism, and radical feminism aren't worth a trip out of the student parking lot, especially when those ideas are made flesh in a warm and loving human being who happens also to be a famous author, who can, simply by her success, make an impression on aspiring student writers. Some might say keep our kids inside, keep them away from seduction, hide them in a campus fort, then line the walls with snipers and fill the wide moat with ravenous beasts who know their catechism. Keep them away from things. Make them think that you'll get everything you want in heaven, except movies, atheists, and guns.

But the agony of being a teacher and a parent is in riding the two sides of a paradox which Christ never explained in sufficient clarity to answer all of our problems: we must be

122

in the world but not of the world. And in following that advice, we need to consider two sometimes contradictory imperatives.

Our children must see the world in which they have been given life—they will know it soon enough. But we must draw lines which separate the city of God from the city of man, lines which delineate, in our own feeble way, the sanctified life of the Christian.

At once, we must push and protect, help our students to ask the great questions and feel the great answers, to see all of God's world without losing the ability to recognize sin.

If we are at all sincere about a Reformed view of Christ and culture, we can't renege on our pledge to redeem institutions which are sin-infected. But if we are at all sincere about being Christians, we must continually remind ourselves that the world is divided into two, not always easily distinguishable, camps.

Someday a man may come along and take Jeremy hunting. Maybe they will walk through field grass grown brittle and dry in autumn winds, and maybe they'll shoot a rabbit for a stew. On that day Jeremy may forget what he had always thought about guns, that they were beyond the reach of God's grace, that they were one piece of this world absolutely beyond redemption. Jeremy may grow into a hunter. Stranger things have happened.

But no matter how old he is, Jeremy needs that old childish sense of guns—that sense that tells him some parts of this world are to be avoided by those people who call themselves children of God's family.

We all need that sense of guns to guide us along the paths of righteousness, because we are not of this world— even though we have been placed squarely within it.

Thanksgiving

"Puritanism," wrote Mencken, "is the sneaking suspicion that someone, somewhere, is having a good time." It may be Mencken's image of the Puritans—scowling, self-righteous zealots—that keeps us from admitting that those New Englanders are the spiritual ancestors of all Reformed folks today.

It may be my fault for not listening closely, but I don't remember anyone telling me—grade school on up—that the Puritans were any relation of ours. No sir. They burned innocent people and called them witches; they jammed people's arms and legs in stocks, right out in public; they generally put the kibosh on any sort of colonial merrymaking.

The fact is, of course, that Dutch surnames merit little more than a footnote in the history of Calvinism in America. Well into the 19th century, most of New England considered itself uprightly Calvinistic, with the exception of a few wayward Unitarians, some Quakers, and a few diabolical antinomians. And that's two hundred years of history, two hundred years of Calvinist American history.

It's only at Thanksgiving that we tape cutouts of smiling men in tall, pointed hats to our elementary school windows, but we call them "pilgrims," not Puritans. A pilgrim sounds more like a searcher than a stinker, even though the word "pilgrim" has its own history of spiritual contexts. Today, the tall, pointed hat of the pilgrim is as much an emblem of Thanksgiving as the tom turkey, tail fully unfurled, as colorful Indian corn, as strange-looking guns

125

with funnels for barrel ends. Even 20th-century Calvinists have commercialized Cotton Mather and his friends in Massachusetts; today, the tall, pointed hat is as much to Thanksgiving as a red-nosed reindeer is to Christmas and a talking rabbit is to Easter.

But we miss some things by refusing to acknowledge our family as family. We miss the fact that Cotton Mather, as wholeheartedly hostile to Arminianism—the set of doctrines repudiated by the famous Synod of Dort way back in the 17th century—as anybody in the Reformed fellowship, once called Arminianism "the grand chokeweed of history"—fairly sharp language for a group whose worst sin was strangling tulips. We miss the fact that the banished Anne Hutchinson, banished from the Colony for following her own inner light, was using our own catechism to indict her holy Puritan neighbors for their "works righteousness." And maybe we miss the real concept of Puritan thanksgiving—not Thanksgiving, but thanksgiving.

Thanksgiving, to the Puritan pilgrims, was a practice, not a red-letter date on the calendar you pick up as a gift from some business person. Thanksgiving was any day, really because thanksgiving was celebrated whenever, wherever it became obvious to our Puritan grandfathers and mothers that the providence of God warranted celebration. The Puritans holidayed far more frequently than we can imagine, given our stereotype of the Puritan frown.

Actually, the Puritans declared thanksgiving days on a whim; maybe it was good crops, but it could just as easily have been good news from the old country, or a ship miraculously saved from destruction on the long trip across, or maybe even a defeat of the Indians—all of these events, and more, called for holidays, and thanksgiving.

Cotton Mather's own tribute to Sir William Phips, for instance, illustrates the real Puritan thanksgiving: ". . . when he had 'great Works' before him, he would invite good men to come and Fast and Pray with him at his house for the success thereof; and when he had undertaken, he would prevail with them to come and keep a Day of 'Solemn Thanksgiving.' " (The emphases belong to Mr. Mather.) Likewise, John Winthrop filled his own diary with records of similar thanksgivings. They were spontaneous; they were assumed obligations; they were often community-wide. Their justification was simple: today God has blessed us, and tomorrow we thank him.

Today, more than 350 years later, thanksgiving is a noun, not a verb. Today we celebrate Thanksgiving because everyone else does, because there's no school, because the government labeled the whole business a four-day weekend, because we always have done it this way. That's okay. There's little worse than self-righteous old Scrooge, especially when he appears, like this, a whole month before his own holiday season.

Besides, we still practice thanksgiving in the old way whenever our local high school basketball team takes a state championship. That's the old idea, of course. But it's just a bit of a shame that we follow the real tradition only then. Maybe if we celebrated thanksgiving as our own spiritual ancestors did, it would be more a response and less of a culture-honed ritual.

Enough. Nostalgia can make fools of us. Just try to keep the turkey moist, the potatoes smooth, the piecrust light and flaky. Besides, there's a whole lot about Cotton Mather—his place in the witchcraft trials, for instance—that his 20th-century grandsons and daughters would much rather forget.

This holiday, give thanks with the whole family, but remember that our Father and all of our Calvinist ancestry would much prefer that we practice thanksgiving than celebrate it.

Comfortable, Familiar, and Ever So Deadly

The broad, square pulpit was straight-cut, fine, light oak, draped with a dark IHS banner like just so many others. A brand-new matching piano graced the left corner of the front of the sanctuary, and three muscular upright chairs, steady as thrones, stood ten feet back of the pulpit on the deep purple carpet. The preacher was handsome, bearded—all the better to relate to kids, I thought.

It wasn't hard to be a visitor. It was so much like home, from the muted chimes of the organ prelude to the announcement of the silent prayer. Comfortable. Familiar. Ever so nice.

A good, rousing psalm, the Law, another song, the debonair dominie singing lustily from the pulpit, an inspiration.

And then he did it. Just as if it were nothing at all, he jerked on the cord of the mike and just came right down to the congregation. He warned no one; he just stepped down, the mike in his left hand, his right hand shaking the cord behind him as if it were some kind of pencil-thin snake. He came right out in front of the two or three empty pews in the ranks, right down off the pulpit. He stood there as if he were no more than one of us.

Nervously, I pulled out the Psalter so I'd have something in my hands. I couldn't decide whether to look at him or not, because it put me on edge; it annoyed me to think that such a handsome preacher would just desert the pulpit and stand there with the rest of us.

And then he asked for prayer requests. A tangible

prickly silence disrupted the perfectly good order of worship. You could feel it roil in your stomach. Finally, a woman, her long hair neat and pretty, told the preacher about her husband right in front of everybody. There was a two-year-old on her lap, and her left arm draped over the shoulder of a kindergartener when she told him about how much she wanted to thank the church for the groceries and such, and ask them all to keep praying for Denny, who, she said, was getting good help at the Center. I didn't hear her too well, but she said something about how Denny himself had admitted the rehabilitation was going well. "Pray for us," she said. "Both of us."

And then he prayed right there from the front. I put down the Psalter and found myself folding my hands, forgetting about the straight-cut oak pulpit, all the familiars, the comfortable knick-knacks of a liturgy become ritual.

I felt scolded. All of this taught me a lesson: complacency, not liberalism, is our foremost enemy. It's atrophy, not unyielding doctrinal purity, that threatens our congregations. Dead orthodoxy is not orthodoxy at all; it is simply dead. The handsome preacher, deserting the pulpit for ten minutes of one worship service, irritated my liturgical sensibilities because I didn't expect him to do it. In my game plan, he was supposed to remain comfortably ensconced behind the pulpit. The young wife's open confession seemed nearly disruptive to the process of worship I have come to expect; in its own way, it offended me because I was unaccustomed to it—I couldn't predict it. It was an alteration in an ordered process that I fully expected to satisfy me long before I had any sense of the content of that process. Years of liturgical traditions have become as comfortable as bedroom slippers, and as easy to slip into and out of.

Complacency, of course, is not cured by a few simple alterations in liturgy—an extra song, a responsive reading or two, even communion by loaf and common cup. Rigor mortis afflicts more than our liturgies. Ironically, it is simply far too easy for a church whose history is built on a rejection of mindless ritual to lapse into it itself, not only in its forms of worship but in the whole practice of its confessional life. The style of our Christian lives becomes too easily the substance of our Christian lives; the medium becomes the message. Too often we send the kids off to the Christian school without having made a real conscious decision to do it. Too often our church programs—Young People's, Men's Society, whatever—exist from year to year simply because they always have. Perhaps too many of us live an unexamined life on the borrowed breath of ancestral generations. And it is so easy to see why: it's simple, and more than that, it's wonderfully comfortable; it becomes, for many of us, "our only comfort."

Just once I would like to hear laypeople and disgruntled preachers in South Holland or Hudsonville or Sioux Center talk about creating a new seminary to fight off the creeping complacency in the church. How many members do we annually lose to the Unitarians? The fact is, we lose many each year to the evangelical churches, and for many of them, it's complacency that sends them packing—too many of the CRC family are willing only to exist.

The believer spends much of his life balancing on this silver wire pulled taut by two ends of a paradox. In this case, tradition, ritual, identity can be a source of life; it gives us a badge, a name, a common reference point. But it can also be a means of death when the form itself becomes the good news.

Some of our friends see the CRC as the Jews of the evangelical movement on this continent: educated, sophisticated, intelligent Christians. That assessment is comforting. But we should not forget that the most Jewish of the Jews were the Pharisees.

Perhaps the only wooden shoes we need to burn are the ones we could not live without, the ones that years of wear have hewn to a comfortable form fit. The klompenhouwer can make new ones, of course, but they might pinch. They might disturb us like the handsome preacher coming down from the pulpit.

Perhaps the greatest irony, the tragic irony, is that everyone who reads this agrees.

Ghost Towns

Halfway between the giant saguaros of Southern Arizona and the ponderosa pines of the San Francisco peaks above Flagstaff, lies a ghost town named Jerome, once the habitation of thousands. The story of Jerome is written in its own topography. An immense chiseled pit, all too reminiscent of Dante's Hell, is gouged deeply into the side of the mountain which walls the city at its western limits. Long ago, from the depths of the mine, tons of valuable mineral deposits came up on box-like railroad cars from hundreds of lantern-capped miners miles into the earth, from Mexican, Chinese, Irish immigrants, from American Indians and blacks and anglos—anyone willing to sweat out a decent paycheck thousands of feet down in the damp sweat of the earth's darkness.

And the city, Jerome, Arizona, gave them life, a home for their families. Service organizations flourished. The tawny shell of a hospital stands on a hill above the city as if awaiting completion.

The old city literally slides down quickly from the mine at the top, following the mountain's edge. At the top, near the hospital and adjacent to the open mine, a ridge of Victorian mansions stand, gabled, balconied, still festooned with the "gingerbread" fancies reminiscent of what Twain called "the Gilded Age." One level beneath, family homes of less pretentious distinction point downward at the Main Street businesses. People who know the story say that one's wealth dictated the level of one's living in Jerome—literally. The wealthy looked down the side of the mountain at the miner's shacks, hundreds of feet below. Today, once one descends from the old business district, one sees few of the single-story shacks that must have leaned against the mountain's side down on the shady side of town, and those that remain can barely be described as "skeletal."

Today Jerome is called a ghost town. People still live in Jerome—artists, silversmiths, hippies, several businessmen who specialize in tourists' weaknesses, a few cowboys, and dozens of dogs. But the town is, for the most part, deserted, its huge mine left behind, a gaping cavity, its underground mining shafts sentried by a rusted derrick.

Jerome is a ghost town. In the hours I've spent on its streets, I've never been frightened by sheeted spectres hovering over the city. I've never heard shrill screams from the old Victorian homes; in fact, I've not seen anything to remind me of the Amityville horrors or Alfred Hitchcock. But Jerome is a ghost town nonetheless, because it has its own mysterious life, its own precarious existence. It is not dead because it is still changing.

Even though its homes are already half gone, even though its hospital admits only the rattlers that slide in from the rocks, even though its Catholic church greets more tourists than parishoners, Jerome maintains its ghostly existence. But it cannot stay in its present state of shambles. If the Victorian homes are not repaired, rebuilt, refurnished, then time and gritty dust and the Arizona sun will slowly reduce them to nothing, just as the houses of the mining proletariat further down the mountain have been long ago humiliated.

In this world nothing stands still, not even a ghost town. I'd like to take my children to Jerome some day, because Jerome is a story, a story one can literally walk through, a cemetery of frame houses that once were homes.

But when my children grow old enough to savor Jerome's own peculiar narrative style, what's left of the old town will be no more. It will either be gone, a victim of time and the elements, or be turned into some neon tourist trap, complete with Ferris wheels, nightclubs, and a Burger King on the edge of town. Nothing stands still, not even a ghost town.

"Nothing gold can stay," Frost once wrote. But the city of Jerome, a ghost town, testifies that silver, copper, turquoise, or wood—and flesh especially—are not immune to the movement of time. Jerome has, you see, only two choices—renewal or disintegration.

It is a lesson from the Ghost of Jerome, the Ghost of Heaven. Nothing stands still, not even a ghost town.

Learning by Heart

My grandmother knew her catechism. She had to. The only way she could make profession of faith in the turn-of-the-century Dutch Reformed Church into which she was baptized, was by knowing question and answer, backwards and forwards. She knew the rigors of the grilling she would get at the hands of the church fathers, so she committed every line and every phrase to her memory, had it down cold.

Back then, the whole business was conducted in Dutch —the language of Adam and Eve. So my grandmother recited the whole regimen of answers in the approved language. One problem. She didn't understand Dutch, so she had only a shadow of an idea what she was professing. She knew only that the answers she slammed into her head were the correct ones. And she passed. Flying colors.

Hindsight is ever clear. It's easy to condemn the church fathers for requiring such an oddity, for it doesn't take a dominie to see that knowing prescribed answers in a language one doesn't understand is like learning to drive a car by riding a horse. The old church was undeniably guilty of the horrendous sin of exacting "rote memorization" from their youthful catechumens. Beastly of them, wasn't it? The very phrase—"rote memorization"—strikes with such horror one might think it was the Nazis who coined it. "Rote memorization" brings back images of schools run by persnickety old school marms, their long hair twisted up tight in a peak atop their pointed heads, bony old wretches armed with hickory switches, who ran dungeon-like one-room schools that kids hated more intensely than dentist's chairs. "Rote memorization"—thank goodness, we've come a long way.

Those one room schools are long gone now. Not far from where I live, one of those few still standing now houses hogs. Once, in a forgotten age before television, those schools stood at the very center of rural life. School programs took farmers out of their fields, set them on well-gouged benches inside, and offered them and their families homegrown and hardly flawless entertainment.

What was the fare? Recitations of Longfellow, long declamations committed to memory by kids barely old enough to milk cows, recitals of famous speeches by adolescents learning rhetorical principles. The whole school performed by memory, by rote memorization. It was, to the parents, splendid entertainment. It is conceivable that at least some of the kids rather enjoyed those evening programs themselves.

The point is, of course, that rote memorization may not have been as beastly, as draconian, as our enlightened sensibilities view it today. Back then, at least some people had fun memorizing.

An alternative means of rendering the phrase "rote memorization" is saying "learning by heart." No educator and no parent, I hope, should reject the exact intention of the words of that phrase. When we ask children to commit a verse to their hearts, we're asking nothing less than to have those words etched forever at the core of their values. Keep it there, we mean—keep it there forever.

My friend's mother suffered a stroke a few months before she died. In those last weeks, it was impossible for her to give her full attention to anyone or anything around her. Sons and daughters came to her room, then left; her conversation moved in and out of consciousness the way prairie winds gust through deserted barns. Quickly, she was losing her grip on her world.

But one thing she could do, almost to the very end. Those sons and daughters would hold her hand and hear her sing, verse upon verse upon verse, of old psalms she had learned, by heart, as a girl. Her childhood of faith had etched those words into her so deeply that when everything else was already gone, the resonance of the psalms were still there. Long ago, she had learned them—by heart.

During my own Bible class training, our pastor thought the catechism wasn't enough to memorize, so he mimeoed some of his favorite psalm lyrics and made us recite them too. Weekly, we'd sing them—lacking both piano and harmony. At the time, I thought being forced to recite all those answers was tortuous enough. The psalms were an unforgivable burden.

Today, sometimes I wish the same misery on my children. We don't often sing old psalms like "Zion, Founded on the Mountains," but when we do I'm proud of not having to look at the book, because the words are mine —no one will ever take them away.

A few lines from Shakespeare, some short poems, a ton of Bible verses, some motley lyrics from pop songs when I was a kid, and a good number of psalms and hymns are written on my heart, some of it by mere repetition and some of it by rote memorization. I'm happy for all of it— even the Beatles.

Perhaps it's time to take another look at rote memorization. It's no secret that memorized lines of great prose and poetry give the holder a vivid and personal sense of the potential beauty of the English language.

But even more important is the non-transferable deed owned by those who have learned by heart. The words, and the values, we set within our children's memories, represent an investment which may someday be rejected—but will never be completely lost.

Death of a Dominie

Today there is a brand new church in Gibbsville, its broad fan-shape somewhat modern, somewhat out of place in a tiny village of maples, old barns, and a cheddar cheese factory. The building may be new, but the church isn't. It's the only church in town and it always has been, for more than a century of Wilterdinks and Van Stelles and Jensemas. In the old days it was part of a denomination that called itself the "Dutch Reformed Church." Today the sign says "Reformed Church in America," but the sign doesn't alter the fact: most of Gibbsville's few hundred citizens are members, and most all of the members are Dutch, even if the "old country" is four or five grand-fathers in the past.

If historians ever bothered with a hamlet like Gibbsville, they would find its history written in three-part homilies; like the history of Puritan New England, Gibbsville's real history is in its sermons, and its leading history-maker has always been its preacher. Gibbsville, Wisconsin, is a one-church town; a one-church, three-business town, now that the village store's front window advertises only the store itself as a bargain. Gibbsville is really little more than a church, and today Gibbsville mourns because its preacher is dead. Gibbsville's "dominie" has died unexpectedly after a little more than two years of leading the church. This afternoon the implement shop is shut down, and the garage has a hand-lettered sign on its front window, telling farmers who aren't at the church they'd better come back in the morning. Today an entire country village mourns

141

together in its new, fan-shaped church.

It is almost 140 years now since an immigrant schooner named the *Phoenix* burned, then sank, in the November-cold Lake Michigan. Some say that more than 200 ruddy-faced Dutch immigrants died less than six miles from Sheboygan harbor, their long journey to a new land that near its destination. Few survived the *Phoenix* tragedy, but some of those who did built the old dusky brick homes around Gibbsville, homes still dated in iron numbers set in brick above the frontroom windows—1861, 1872. Sudden, unexpected, tragic death is not new here in Gibbsville.

But the survivors of the *Phoenix* brought a distinctive kind of Calvinist piety with them, a piety that lives like some old resident in the village yet today, and sets Gibbsville apart from a hundred hamlets like it on Wisconsin's county roads. There's no Schlitz sign here, no Pabst, no Blatz, no corner bar that advertises packaged goods and Tombstone frozen pizzas. No one does business on Sunday in Gibbsville. No one mows lawns or rakes leaves on Sunday. On the Sabbath no one discs the cornfields that fortify the village. Sunday is church day.

Beneath that old-fashioned piety is a kind of 20th-century Calvinism evident in the words of the preacher who today comforts a whole town assembled in the new church. He talks of the sovereignty of God, a doctrinal tenet which insists that God is in control of everything down here, including, almost ironically, the death of a preacher. Sovereignty is a tough thing to swallow at a time like this, but Gibbsville has heard the doctrine sounded from its pulpits for more than a century of preachers. It's a strange, paradoxical thing: God has ordained the death of the preacher, yet God must be praised because he does control the world.

Today, in church, the emotions of an entire village balance precariously on a paradox—their very human need to lament the loss of their preacher, and their faith-grounded knowledge that today the man is where he wanted to be, forever. A painful joy as tangible in the new sanctuary as the long, hardwood pews brings tears to the eyes of broad-shouldered dairymen and turns the inquisitive head of a little boy, who stares at the red and swollen and very strange eyes of his big sister. It's an odd thing in this media age—an age of "That's Incredible" and "Three's Company" and media politicians. It's odd because it's a real story, the heart-strong story of an entire village, the grief and faith of Gibbsville, a story too noble, perhaps, for our times.

After leaving the church, Gibbsville drives to the cemetery in the rain that falls from a sullen, gray sky. Long ago it wasn't uncommon for people to believe that their world cried when they did. Hundreds of years later no one believes such an antiquated notion.

But to see a whole town, complete, standing in October rain and wind, witnessing a final committal, saying good-bye to its preacher, a good preacher, is to a question our own scientific smugness.

Today, all of Gibbsville wept.

The Immigrant

I was reared in the old way; as a child I was to be seen and not heard. But the old way had side benefits, even for kids. Occasionally attentive ears were privy to adult conversation, because to be seen and not heard is close to being completely forgotten. I remember one coffee and cookie conversation on a Sunday morning after church, sitting around the kitchen table—late spring, maybe '53 or '54. I sat there quietly with a cookie, listening to my folks talk about Calvin College with a pair of students from town, home from there for the summer.

"So many wetbacks over there this year," one of those kids said, sneering.

My mother didn't understand. I could see it in her eyes. So did the college kid.

"We call 'em wetbacks because they're just off the boat," he told her. He thought it was funny. So we all laughed, because laughing at supposed inferiors comes easy to us, I suppose, especially when we don't know them.

When the students were gone, I asked my father what a wetback was.

"An immigrant," he said, "somebody just over from Holland."

Today we've buried an immigrant; we've laid her body in frozen prairie earth in a village cemetery thousands of miles from that woman's childhood, an ocean and more away from the world of her parents. Her own children are all grown now; they have their own families. They've developed homes and established roots of their own. But her husband is left here, and he is still an immigrant. Today he is alone.

"We should have come to Canada," she told me once, nodding as if there were absolutely no question about their mistake.

It was no indictment against America, really—no vindictive condemnation of political principles or cultural values. She said it because she knew she was a wetback, an immigrant, someone not entirely at home here in America. But she knew, with a similar conviction, that the old country was somewhere far behind her, no more a home, perhaps, than this country. She could live no more comfortably here in America than back there in Holland. Her life on earth ended here, two days before Christmas, on the snowy, rolling prairie, in a country she adopted for the sake of her children, a foreign country—a country as strange to her as Holland is today, a quarter century after she left.

She knew she was an immigrant, and she knew that Canada has more immigrants, more folks like her husband and herself, more kindred souls sharing the odd limbo of an immigrant life—strangers somewhat awkwardly at home in a strange land.

I didn't know any immigrants when I was a boy. There was only one old lady in our church whose speech was warbled by an accent, and she was something of a witch to me, not a good-looking woman, slightly eccentric, a woman my father claimed couldn't shake the old world idea that she was upper class. So I knew nothing about immigrants—nothing except the notion that immigrants were something of an embarrassment—"wetbacks," those college kids had called them.

During my own college years I met immigrants personally. They generally had fewer clothes than Americans, so they didn't dress quite up to snuff. Often they had peculiar accents. Generally, they were more bold in the classroom, more determined, more committed than those of us who thought of college as a high school with only slightly more homework.

Through the years I listened to them explain what they

called their Perspective—some kind of unifying philosophy they used to measure ideas and even people—a kind of tool for determining righteousness. To me, a perspective was a place up on a hill where you could see for miles. Perspective, I learned, was to them something more than a scenic overlook.

And they had that language, of course. Sometimes they'd laugh at word jokes no American could begin to understand. And sometimes I knew they were laughing at us—the Americans, for our own ways, maybe for simply being American.

My grandmother was a life-long member of the American Legion Auxiliary because her brother was killed by a grenade in France just a couple months before Armistice day, 1918. My own father spent two uniformed years of his life in the Pacific theater during World War II, as did a number of my uncles and aunts. To me, being an American was something of a favored blessing bestowed by generations of Dutch-surnamed soldier patriots. But to those immigrants I knew in college, to be an American meant something else—something less than a rich blessing. To be an American meant to be the passive recipient of a vision of life that wasn't always in harmony with that weapon they called their Perspective. There was nothing really wrong with being an American, but, to them, there was something wrong, terribly wrong, with thinking like an American. I had never been aware that there could be a difference. My first reaction was to think that the immigrants were thinking like Hollanders, not like North Americans. Years, it took, for me to understand that what they called Perspective had little to do with country of residence or origin.

I sat through hours of war stories, stories of the cancerous Nazis eating away at the life of the country for too many long years. Over coffee richly creamed, I heard countless stories, recent stories, of what it was like to come over with no money and no language—the societal poverty created by lack of the commodity of words. And slowly the mind of the immigrant began to emerge from the caricature of the wetback. Slowly, that mind shaped my own, forced me to question my loyalties, pushed me to look at a world larger than the four-square dimensions of a quiet and supportive village of mirrors where the greatest theological enemies were the folks in the church down the block, the one you didn't attend.

The woman we've buried today once told me this story. She became very concerned about a strike somewhere in Northwest Iowa—maybe Iowa Beef. And one day she told a lady from her church—"We ought to be praying about that situation," she said.

Her friend looked at her. "But there's no one from our church involved, is there?" her friend said.

The world of difference between those two comments is itself a portrait of the new world faced by the immigrant, a new and strange place where fellow worshippers, folks who recited the Apostles Creed together, didn't always see themselves or their world or their place within it in similar ways.

At least three forces shaped the immigrant mind in ways that Americans don't clearly understand. First, Abraham Kuyper, part dominie, part journalist, part politician—an immensely pious man who pushed Christians out of their church-walled security and into the world. From Kuyper those immigrant students gleaned what they called their Perspective.

Second, the Nazis—a horrid mass of uniformed worms who devoured everything but the spirit of their Dutch hosts. The Netherlands was occupied during the war, occupied by a brute force that ground Dutch life to a halt for five years. This woman's confession of stealing to stay alive during those years—that confession I will never forget.

And third, the experience of immigration itself. Immigration can sound so noble when it happened to ancestors whose brown-toned pictures collect dust on our library shelves. But immigration is displacement—the willful severance of family ties, national loyalties, and the heritage of home itself, plus the concurrent immersion in a culture altogether new and foreign and sometimes even hostile—immigrants are, let's remember, wetbacks.

148

My own immigrant great-grandfather is buried a dozen miles from here in another village cemetery. More than a century ago he took his family across—wetbacks. So for one hundred years my family has been American. Today, Terschelling, the little island he came from, is to me little more than a picture on a travel brochure. Four generations of Schaaps have settled into this country's way of life. America is, for better or for worse, my home; in these flatlands are my own ethnic and familial roots, as well as those of most of this immigrant woman's children.

Only a few months ago I sat on a long wooden bench set in a museum in Philadelphia. The bench had been taken from Ellis Island, New York, the first stop for millions of European immigrants in the late 19th century. At one time ancestors from both sides of my family must have sat waiting on those very benches for some American official to call out Dutch names he couldn't hope to pronounce correctly.

Sitting there on that bench thrilled me, took me back to what must have been an anxious and fearful time in my own family's history, a time I could only imagine, sitting there as they must have. But try as I might, I will never know the cross-currents of being adopted into another country—of being an immigrant, a wetback.

Today we laid a body to rest in frozen earth that is for her no more a home than this Iowa prairie ever was. And yesterday two grieving parents left an infant child in some adjacent plot in the same acre of land. Finally all of us are immigrants—no matter how far back we can trace our proud ancestry. No one stays on this earth.

I remember a plaque that used to hang upstairs in my childhood home. The words were in English, but this woman we've buried today knew its lesson in two languages. "Only one life will soon be past," it said; "Only what's done for Christ will last."

That Perspective, rooted in Christ's gift of grace, turns us all into wetback pilgrims.

Marking Time

For years I've envied Henry David Thoreau. "Time," he said, "is but the stream I go a-fishing in." Of course, his world, 19th century America, was hardly the technological complex of today. "We are so institutionalized," a man once told me, speaking of his church, "we organize meetings to organize meetings." But Thoreau may well have known such a world himself; in fact, his self-imposed exile at Walden Pond was an attempt to avoid the rat race: "I went to the woods because I wished to live deliberately, to front only the essential facts of life, and see if I could not learn what it had to teach, and not, when I came to die, discover that I had not lived."

We are, *all* of us, creatures of time, and too often we are its slaves. Even Thoreau marked his Walden sojourn by the metronome of the seasons, a more "natural" rhythm, perhaps, than the modern tickless digitals with radio alarms; but a means, nonetheless, of marking time.

Chaucer's characters lived under the reign of their own strange notions of time. Folks in the Middle Ages saw themselves in a egocentric world where the circling planets were thought somehow to control certain segments of time—not the hours of the day, but the "hours unequal," the hours from sunrise to sunset, and on from sunset to sunrise again. These "unequal hours" were thought to be governed by the character of the planets in the heavens. We are heirs to that ancient vision of planetary control at least in the manner by which we name our days: Saturn-day, Sun-day, Moon-day, for instance.

151

We might conclude that medieval notions of time were even more tyrannical than our own clocks, for a birthdate in the middle of some planetary configuration sometimes was thought even to affect the probable career of the child: butchers, hangmen, tailors, barbers, cooks, cutlers, carpenters, physicians, and members of sundry other professions were thought clumped together under the aegis of Mars.

Such determinism, we moderns say, is interesting, in retrospect, but obviously silly. Yet each age creates its own tyrannical icons to mark time, and govern our use of it. Not long ago I sat in the home of an immigrant woman whose living room decorations explained both her past and her personality. Hung above her library was what she called, in Dutch, her *schipperke*, a time-keeping, hand-carved allegory, really, and according to that lady, pretty much standard front room decor, years ago, in Dutch homes near the North Sea.

Even if you've not seen the clock, you know the allegory. An Atlas type—huge, rippling muscles—bears the weight of the entire planet on his right shoulder, and he is grimacing, one knee already down and the other bent beneath him, as if he is near collapse. Two angels appear to float to either side of the planet, trumpeting some wordless warning to anyone who glances at the time. No words are imprinted there, but the drama in wood figures explains itself. The angels in flowing robes announce their moral in the thick ticking of the *schipperke*. Atlas weakens, folks— they say—so number your days, make the most of the time, the end is near. Coast dwellers on the North Sea were no less ruled by time than Chaucer's lively folk, it seems.

But today we really are no different. Recently I bought a new digital watch with a stopwatch function, because after a year of jogging I thought I had built up enough courage to know how terribly slow I was running. Right there on the face of this watch is a little bell; after an hour of reading of the instructions, I discovered that the little bell meant that one silly chirp would come out of this black-strapped, technological marvel, every hour on the hour, all day and all night, all month for that matter—as long as the tiny battery would emit juice enough to make it squeak.

So today, every hour, the cheap watch gives me an odd chirping reminder that another hour of my life is gone. That crazy watch is intimidating. Right in the middle of my morning it will chirp unexpectedly—one silly high-pitched bark—and force me to stop whatever I'm doing and remind me that counting only our days is not enough in the 1980's. Today, I'm counting my hours, thanks to a twenty dollar wizard that locks on to my wrist.

And I'm not alone. There's a gent in our Sunday School whose watch is more musically inclined than mine. When mine chirps, his answers with a chimed chorus. Right in the middle of a discussion of miracles, an hour's passing triggers an audible reminder that time hasn't stopped, not even for Jairus's daughter. We go on as if nothing has happened, but the audio reminders seem to slap us all awake to the fact that this discussion has gone on long enough. There remain things to be done, even on a Sabbath afternoon.

Although the hand-carved artistry is lacking in this piece of Japanese technology, the day-numbering moral of the *schipperke* is still here in the lousy chirping. Who says we moderns really control time today? Time still pushes us, structures our days and nights—and sometimes locks us in cages we seem as powerless to identify as escape. Today, could any minister preach longer than a half-hour or shorter than fifteen minutes, without some befuddled congregation furrowing their brows and wondering about his state of mind? I just can't help but envy Thoreau, even if I'm skeptical of his platitudes.

Besides, timepiece noise isn't news. It was batteries and electricity that made the pendulum extinct. Years ago, I imagine, in that ancient world before television, every home had a ticking clock, and there's no significant difference between my chirping wristwatch and a tick-tocking grandfather in a tall oak cabinet.

Anyway, who says the chirping or the ticking or the struggling Atlas is moral admonition? Maybe it's the hearer's sense of guilt that translates time's movement into a perpetual scolding. After all, I still haven't decided whether this chirping signals another hour gone or another hour coming—whether I should lament my inactivity or firm up my resolve, this new hour, to do more. Every hourly chirp may simply mean another hour's opportunity —if I adopt my fair share of positive thinking.

History shows us numerous illustrations of Calvinism's flirtation with the materialistic excesses of capitalism. Paul's admonition to make the most of our time is too easily translated into what has been called "the work ethic," a phrase not always comfortably separate from the old nemesis we called "works righteousness." A whole lot of us could use a little respite, a little time off for fishing at Walden Pond, an hour or two to remember how liberated we are from Chaucer's old determinism.

I once heard a story about a man called by a whole village of offspring simply "Grandpa Pete." His hearing was gone by the time he was eighty-plus, and he never seemed to understand that he talked louder than anyone else in order to be sure of his own words. One day Grandpa Pete buried one of his sons, a younger man who was himself a grandfather. A second son helped him to the funeral home, up the steps, and through the room to the open casket where he saw, for the last time, his own boy's face.

He turned to the man holding his arm. "Yeah, John," he said, "Matt beat us to it, didn't he?" He said it loud enough for the whole world to hear.

Grandpa Pete never had a chirping watch, I'm sure. And, more than likely, Grandpa Pete never heard of Henry David Thoreau. But somehow I can't help thinking that Grandpa Pete would have got along just fine at Walden Pond, and I know this much—he did like fishing.

Winter Thaw

Surly prairie folks like to say that "thirty below keeps out the riff-raff," as if strength of character is a fringe benefit of simply enduring a lifetime's succession of Great Plains winters. While the logic may be faulty, anyone who has notched a reasonable number of flatland Januarys can recognize the spirit that animates such a bare-knuckled claim. A prairie winter is no picnic, ever. If it's not a polar air mass freshly spun from the arctic, it's those merciless winds numbing cheeks, chilling fingers, and turning chapped lips stiff and brittle, so kids have to cry when they smile. Or it's the rage of blizzards rattling storm windows and choking the yard in drifts that swoop around every nook and corner. Winter stands a criminal on the prairie, sometimes even a murderer.

My father-in-law insists that every year there's something called a "January thaw." He's spent many more winters on the prairie than I have, so he ought to know, but I don't believe him anyway. In January, sundogs glitter in the sky on wind-still mornings, and month-old snow beneath your boots chirps and cracks with every step. The bright and sunny cold locks you in winter's tight fist, and April seems less a promise than a fond memory. "Winter thaw?—baloney. Not this year." That's the kind of gruffness prairie winters build into character.

But this year he was right. Something of March came in on a December southern breeze. The Calvinist in me wants to say that we Siouxlanders did not merit such mercy— maybe it was a gift for working through such a horrible

155

harvest season. Whatever it was, the sun poked through arctic air, thawed a couple of frosty inches from the land, and sent clear streams of snow melt rushing through the street gutters. Winter thaw shook the chill out of cold fingers, and brought half the town to a Saturday auction sale right on our block, the house kitty-cornered from the bank's flashing sign of time and temperature. People said it wasn't a day to stay inside—not with such perfect winter weather.

I'm ashamed to confess it, but I wasn't aware of my neighbor's death. When I saw the bill of sale in the paper, I realized she was gone—an eighty-year-old widow who drove a spotless seventy-three Pontiac only to church and back, a childless, usually smiling woman, married close to fifty years to a village merchant. But I wasn't aware of her death. She must have died no more than five hundred feet from our family room, and I didn't even know. I wondered what matter of business I was up to when it happened. Even in the middle of a winter thaw, the chill of my own insular life seemed deep and frigid when I saw the bill of sale and realized what had happened.

And it was more than warm temperatures that brought us all out to pillage the spoils of death itself. There it was —a woman's entire life laid out on tables in three parallel lines—her kitchen and her bedroom, her best silver and most precious doilies, her husband's rings and pocket-watches, their embroidered pillowcases, their framed marriage certificate—all of it dropped in corn flakes boxes or lying naked on a flatbed wagon, booty for a gawking crowd in the unseasonal warmth of a winter thaw.

Auctions turn men into vultures sometimes, turn us all into centurions, casting lots for the leftovers to the rhythmic chant of the auctioneer. What's the right price for an old framed Dutch lithograph—the Broad and the Narrow way —intricately detailing an age-old allegory, complete with Biblical references in tiny, perfect script? What's the price of a life's investment in the morality pictured there? Some antique dealer with money picks it up, looking to turn a quick twenty dollar profit. Childless, my neighbor deserted a home on earth and left everything, every precious memory in delft or porcelain or brass, and the burly auctioneer stepped through all of it with a dollar, dollar-now-two. And crowding up to the flatbed on a front lawn grown slick in mud, we bought and bought until nothing but slate walls and block foundation and a shingled roof remained of a home become, once more, a house. Some kinds of chills nip at more than your nose.

"It'll be a sizeable estate," a man told me in hushed tones, standing there next to what remained of their marriage bed. This auction was different than many others, because the childless couple had long ago decided that all of their material wealth would be given to charities —mostly church organizations. So this death brought a windfall for missions, and that burly auctioneer translated every trinket memory into spiritual opportunity somewhere down the road. Almost made our bidding noble in the winter thaw.

It was over by five. All the easy chairs were trucked home to new living rooms, all the thumbed over collectables were part of new den collections, and all the old man's garden tools were hung in garages elsewhere in town. Some of the women may have made Sunday dinners in my neighbor's pots and pans. When the sun reined in the last tint of western glow, the house turned as dark and empty as it had been years ago, when the painters picked up their pails and brushes and left nothing but spotless walls behind them.

Two childless lives were gone, almost completely, from this world—from our very block, their legacy lovingly become part of church coffers.

Saturday night we ate steaks out of town at a new restaurant—good, thick steaks. But after we returned home and I put the car away, I stopped and looked at the house on the corner. It was late and dark, and the white roof gleamed in the glow of a corner streetlamp. Peeking just over the roof, the bank's clock clicked out the time and temperature—time and temperature—time and a temperature that seemed, despite the winter thaw, to be cheerless, January cold.

Two blessings come with every winter thaw—a reprieve

from the tightness of the cold, and the warm-breathed whisper that, despite January's battering, spring will come. It's a promise. Even though her house is empty and dark, I rest assured that my neighbor knows on this winter night what it means to be out of the cold, and that knowledge is enough to warm the chill from my own bones, even out here in the prairie.

To Do, Or Not To Be

Our four-year-old son doesn't like the trauma of reciting Sunday School verses publicly—at least that's what his too-lenient father thinks. Every Sunday morning after breakfast, his parents haul out his Sunday School paper and try to push the little verse into his memory, hoping he'll hip-pocket the words for an hour or so and earn another gold star behind his name on the wall chart in his classroom.

"Say it now, Davey, come on," we beg him.

He shakes his head and acts his antsy best, trying to avoid the stage we've set for him. I don't blame him. I never put much stock in memorization, remembering the tricks I used to pull myself to make it appear I knew my catechism.

"Come on," his mother urges. "Trust in the Lord . . ."

He bites on her prompting. "Trust in the Lord . . . and . . . be good."

"*DO* good," his mother says. "Trust in the Lord and *DO* good."

Boredom appears on his face in long drawn lines. "*BE* good?—*DO* good?—big deal," his eyes say. And his father says so too. After all, it's getting close to church time now. What Sunday School teacher would keep a four-year-old from a gold star for one silly word—and a two letter word! —in a memory verse. We don't recruit our teachers from the marines.

But the silly distinction stays with me, and I suppose I can blame its haunting me on my profession. After teaching grammar for as long as I have, my mind simply inhales such sentences and pares them like some kitchen wonder. *BE,* the rhetorician in me says, in this case is technically an intransitive verb—it can take no object. *DO,* meanwhile, is transitive. So, all the way to church, my English teacher's brain draws distinctions between the "good" of my son's version of his memory verse, and the "good" of the Sunday School text.

Already thickened with parental homilies on not letting his toys lie around and not forever bugging his older sister, Davey's four-year-old mind interprets the verse to make *GOOD* an adjective (of course he doesn't know that terminology yet) describing his own behavior. It makes more sense to him to *BE GOOD*—that is, to describe himself as *GOOD,* than to *DO GOOD.*

In the Sunday School version, *DO,* a transitive verb, makes *GOOD* a noun—something you *DO*—not necessarily something you are. Four long years of life aren't enough to prompt him to see a difference. But, by the time we pile out of the car at church, I become rather painfully aware of the subtle difference which too often exists between the Davey version and the text itself, because I know that some very good, respectable people *DO* very little good; and I also know that some folks who *DO* a great deal of good themselves may not, late on Saturday nights, *BE* good themselves. Some things a grown-up would rather not know.

My son, it seems, has put his little finger on a real problem, I'm thinking. Many of us have come from an ethnoreligious tradition which valued my son's sentiment very highly, a tradition where *BEING GOOD* may well have been thought to be the high calling of the Christian life.

Many of my students, for instance, when asked to characterize their own Christian tradition of living, will do it in a litany of don'ts: "we are different from others because we don't work (or play) on Sunday, or we don't go to the public school, or we don't have dances, or we don't gamble on weekend trips to Las Vegas." Their own great-grandparents would likely have penned a much longer list: no scissors on Sunday, no card-playing (except Rook), no theater-going, no Sabbath potato-peeling. Sitting in my own church, I am reminded, by my son's misquote, of a word that has become something of an embarrassment to many of us—piety. "Trust in the Lord and *BE* good" sounds like a commandment of restraint—don't be naughty. "Oh, be careful little feet where you walk," we used to sing so happily, sure that some turf was inherently evil. "How would you like to be in a movie house when Christ comes again?"—that sort of thing.

But the Reformed tradition has quietly undergone its own Vatican II, without the hoopla. The old verities, codified into something roughly akin to Mosaic law, are forever gone. Reformed folks don't bully their non-Reformed neighbors into keeping the lawn mowers in the garage on the Sabbath anymore; if the truth be known, many of them go boating together. Is such a turn of events indication of a clear lapse in orthodoxy? Some would claim so, but the changes are more complex. An old-world ethic is dying as its descendents slip—like an early spring swimmer—into the mainstream of North American life. Is that regrettable? Perhaps it is, but it is equally inevitable.

While Davey's mistake reminds me of our own past, the Sunday School text characterizes the present in our tradition, as it rightly should. Annually, we celebrate World Hunger Sunday. Annually, Synod holds forth on racial prejudice, nuclear proliferation, war in general, South African apartheid, the revolution in Nicaragua, and fifty-seven other varieties of injustice. Today, CRWRC rivals the Back to God Hour as the denominational fair-haired child; somewhere behind lags Foreign Missions and Home Missions, both begging for committed people to fill vacancies. Reformed service organizations, created years ago to take care of "our own," today consider broader mandates and serve the needs of a world much larger than those folks between the covers of a family album.

We have, perhaps as much in reaction to our own intensive inwardness as in response to Biblical mandate, become a denomination concerned with and serious about *DOING GOOD*, an organized network of brother's keepers. "Trust in the Lord and *DO* good." Denominationally, we merit a star because we seem to have the verse down correctly, although many among us might claim that we still aren't *DOING* enough.

The problem is that Davey doesn't understand *DOING GOOD* yet. He'll have to get older before he'll understand concepts like justice, before he can feel the joy of sharing, before he understands that there is a place like South Africa, and before he feels the despair of unemployment. Today, he lives on Sesame Street.

And that's what I'm thinking about this morning before the service. Regeneration, I've been taught, occurs in two steps. First, there is justification—that act of God by which he cleanses us individually from our sin and brings us to Him; then sanctification—the long road of godliness that each of us, both alone and in community tries to walk, living through the implications of having been redeemed. Sanctification, in Davey, will begin—we pray—within himself; and, as he matures, it will broaden into Latin American studies and the Genevan nuclear arms negotiations. It will occur in a parallel to his breaking through the barriers of time and place which his successive phases limit him to. He will learn, we trust, to *DO* good, as he becomes aware of a world larger than Sesame Street and the confines of his Sunday School class.

But first he will have to be justified. He will have to feel the cleansing power of God's blood in his soul. He will, I believe, have to learn that God's will for his own life starts with himself. I think that's why he said today—at only four years old—*BE* instead of *DO*.

And it hurts me, this morning in church, to think that the advance in *DOING* good may have been made at the expense of our understanding of and interest in *BEING* good. The world is no less evil than it was in 1928. But we lack, today, a means of defining how to *BE GOOD* in our world. The grandchildren of pious forebears have money and power and prestige in these 1980s, but many of them—including myself—find it somewhat easier to pontificate on global injustice than to know whether it's right or wrong to forget about Sunday night services—after all, they're little more than an ethnic tradition, aren't they?

162

Piety may be, even today, the foundational strength of God's kingdom-builders. The sometimes cloyingly pious writings of Abraham Kuyper, that immensely important man to our tradition, may well be the only work of his that speaks clearly to all of us in this North American culture. "To be near unto God," he wrote in the book by the same name, "can never be anything else than the outcome and the fruit of our own personal spiritual life."

DOING GOOD is, in effect, *BEING GOOD.* But *BEING GOOD* almost certainly comes first. Trouble is, in our churches today, lots of us aren't so sure of what *BEING GOOD* means anymore. We used to know, but we can't go back to yesterday—no one can.

All of 1928 is behind us now—theater, dance, cards— and we've put nothing concrete in its place except social action. Many of us aren't sure anymore how to *BE GOOD,* or whether, indeed, it makes any difference at all, as long as we hate racism, nuclear war, and world hunger.

So right now Davey's sitting in the pew drawing a picture while the preacher is praying up front. Years ago, perhaps, some fathers would not have tolerated such sacrilege. I let it go today—I don't want to condition him to hate church, after all. Who is right? Does a grandfather's strictness build a respect for communal prayer? Does my leniency make worship less formidable and, down the road, more appealing? Who is right? I don't know. I'm not sure of the practice of piety, at least not so sure as he might have been.

Anyway, I hope my son remembers the verse, but I don't much care whether he says it with a *BE* or a *DO.* Maybe I am too easy on him. But I doubt his teacher will refuse him a star because of his error.

More than anything else, I hope that someday he'll be able to say it both ways.

Leap-Frogging

I've always thought that bringing wiggly, half-pint kids along to symphonies and plays is slightly pretentious and more than a little silly. But then, who am I to judge? I take my kids to cemeteries. We all hug our own values as dearly as we do our children, I suppose, and urge our kids—sometimes even shove them—onto paths we ourselves feel noble or noteworthy, as if they were requirements in our own family curriculums.

Last May I didn't give my kids a choice. I slapped them in the car with their grandfather and me and a couple pots of bright red geraniums, and off we went to the local cemetery. It's something of a ritual in the small town where I was reared: the day before Memorial Day folks replace last year's pots of wilted stalks with a new spring splash of color, setting them in gingerly, right there at the base of the stones of loved ones. I wanted my kids to see my father on his knees, trowel in hand, and I wanted them to sense something of the oddly-hallowed ground where their own unknown great-grandparents were laid.

The experience didn't charge them with respect—not in the least. From the edge of the hill where the cemetery stands, they could see the belt of lake water run straight as a ruler all along the horizon to the east. Freshly-tilled farmland patched the meadows stretching into the woods that underline the seam of lake and sky. The cemetery grass was freshly cut, the stones shiny in the soft yellow dusk of early spring, and the whole place seemed to them little more than a brand new playground, complete with obstacle course—a hundred different solid shapes in rows, perfect for climbing, even riding like stone ponies.

The whole event didn't generate reverence like I hoped it would. In a minute they were playing tag or hide-and-seek. When they started in on leap-frog, I finally collared them. I tried to explain how such merry-making was not in good taste, but they didn't understand. They could just as well have been listening to a granite monument.

Maybe I'll try it again next May. They'll be a year older.

Today I'm reminded of last Memorial Day. Today I stood out here in another graveyard, hundreds of miles away, at the internment of a man I knew through a year of Sunday night Bible studies. There was no leap-frog out here, only the tension of a few quiet last words whispered in the rough winds that snapped the canvas edges of the canopy over the grieving family and friends.

Several years ago we were the youngest couple in a Sunday night Bible study. Once a month we lined up against some older saintly types, and after a few minutes of genial banter, we'd all drop the gloves and do battle, scrapping away for fair. It didn't matter if we were studying Genesis or Revelation, eventually everything boiled down to the very touchy issues fraught with odd sounding titles and all sorts of vivid emotions—the historical nature of Scripture or the problem of headship. Every Sunday we battled away on whether or not women should be preachers. There was a certain inevitability to the final destination of our discussion, just as there was no question how we'd line up on the touchy issues. The youngest in the bunch, my wife and I felt no fear in pushing the old folks; we even pleasured in it, prodding, nudging, even teasing sometimes, sure that our well-meant rebelliousness wouldn't scar the quality of the older folks' faith or the strength of their devotion.

Sometimes things settled down during coffee; sometimes they didn't. Those were enjoyable discussions, even though none of us ever changed our minds about anything in the heat those tired old arguments could still muster. When you're the youngest, you can be as bothersome as a pesky horsefly, because no one expects you to have any answers. We loved that kind of freedom. The stoic faith of the older folks always lay there beneath us like a cushion—no matter how far away we'd fly, we'd know exactly where those saintly types would be when we came down. Their dogged conservatism gave us freedom. It was nice.

Today we're in a different church. The old one grew too big, so a hundred families started over fresh. We don't have many old folks in this new church; they all stayed with the old one. That's understandable.

So we're in a new Bible study now, and all the members are younger than we are—except John and Anne, and John is the man we buried today. This new Bible study is worlds apart from the old one. Not once all year long did anyone mention women in office; not once all year did anyone bring up the authority of Scripture or the nature of headship. We don't fight. We never fight. When these younger folks ask questions, they don't want arguments—they want answers.

I suppose that's all right. I rather miss putting up the dukes with the old saints, but what I dislike most is the fact that when I look around, just about everyone I see is younger than I am. Maybe two or three meetings it took for me to realize that I don't ask any questions any more—I answer them. All through last year's Bible studies, my wife and I—and John and Anne—were set like stone beneath the path of the conversation. If things were unresolved or confusing, much more youthful faces than ours turned to us for answers. Don't get me wrong, I liked the Bible study, but I'm not always comfortable with this new role—a walking, talking catechism text.

Today I'm scared a little, because now John is dead. Being out here reminds me of my kids playing games in the cemetery, but it also reminds me of something my father once told me.

"Sometimes you get to wonder where all the faithful people have gone—men like John Luteyn," he said once, several years ago, as if it were an editorial. "People like that were powerful believers."

Today, at John's funeral, I know exactly what my father was feeling that day, because when I think of our Bible study, I feel the loneliness he let plague him that day. John's death makes me feel deserted, in a way.

But I also remember what I was thinking in the middle of my own father's lament. He knew this John Luteyn in a way that I didn't. To me, Luteyn was little more than an old white-haired man who sat in the same church bench every Sunday, maybe the last man in church who could sing the Psalms in Dutch.

To my father, there may have been no more John Luteyns. To me, a whole generation behind, there still was. In fact, my father stood—and stands—himself in the roll call of saints written in my own head. My father is to me what John Luteyn was to him. And so was my Bible study friend John—the John we've buried out here today.

And all of this makes me think that perhaps I was wrong in chewing out my children for their graveyard game of leap-frog. It may well have not been in good taste, but in spirit, I guess, it was right. Because I hope, like those parents who wrestle their kids along to symphonies, that my own children walk those paths that I want them to—feel the comfort and strength in the faith of their own grandparents. That's at least part of the reason I brought them along to the graves of their believing great-grandparents, I guess—no matter how odd it must have been to two kids who turned the cemetery into a playground.

It's not a game really, but it is a kind of leap-frog we play. Those elderly people we respect for their devotion to God are themselves monuments of faith, whether they be alive or dead. And they stand in our minds as stone-strong testimonies of the glory of belief and assurance.

But they are there to leap too, because once they are gone we cannot stand still and lament their passing. We can't stand in the shadow of a tree that's been felled. It is probably less exciting to be answering questions than to be continually asking them. But someone has to do that job.

Today I feel the fear those saintly types may have carried into the old Biblical battles, because John is gone.

The rest of us may well stand here with both hands on the coffin today, but it's September and another church

year is beginning, another round of monthly Sunday night Bible studies. Like it or not, we all must jump like the kids, push ourselves up on the strength of the monuments and then vault over—and even beyond.

Harsh as it sounds, it's what they'd want us to do. That much we know for sure.

Homecoming

Visiting recently in the state of Washington, we were told of one family's plans for this summer's vacation, plans not unique, perhaps, in this day of the search for roots. Rather than a mule ride down Grand Canyon, a tour of Disneyland, a camping trip to Yosemite, or a weekend in Vegas, our friends were planning a visit (with full consent of their children) to Douglas County, South Dakota, and Pipestone County, Minnesota, just two nearly indistinguishable spots on the midland prairie where their nearly forgotten grandparents had once been homesteaders. In a sense, they were planning a trip home—to a home that neither Mom nor Dad could ever remember. Their plans reminded me of my own "homecoming" during last summer's vacation.

My uncle, whose family stories fascinated me as a child, explained in a letter that his grandfather was buried in Orange City, or so he had been told. "Could you look for it," he asked, as if the request might force an unnecessary intrusion into my summer, "and if you find it, snap a picture?"

Since my uncle's grandfather, and my great-grandfather, C.C. Schaap, had lived much of his life in eastern Iowa, I was as amazed at the revelation as I was eager to hunt for the marker out here in the northwest corner of the state. The Homecoming prospect of finding the stone of C.C. Schaap, the gaunt ex-sailor whose bearded presence looms over the homestead picture we still have in our library, was, to me, very compelling. More than that, it was thrilling for me to think that I might be able to stand that close to someone whose physical presence I had missed by more than a half century, but whose blood, however diluted with strains Hartman, Hemkes, and Dirkse, still flowed within me, and whose name I not only shared but had perpetuated, with the recent arrival of a son, for at least one more generation.

The stone looked almost new. I found it after nearly two hours of walking, reading, and scraping, in a section of the cemetery that seemed almost new, void of the old, crooked marble ghosts whose inscriptions had been dulled by the passage of prairie seasons. "C.C. Schaap" it said at the top of a barrel-like monument that stood unflinchingly in the heat of an early June afternoon, its glossy sides flashing in the sun.

And there was for me, at that moment, an overwhelming sense of home, despite the fact that I had never stood there before. I felt nervous, reluctant, almost fearful, for although no other human breathed there at that moment, there was to me an unmistakable sense of life before me, life in no modern American sense, but in perpetuity. So I stood, smiling, in the sharply cut grass of the Orange City cemetery, laughing at myself, or at the part of me that seemed to fear a nonexistent but nonetheless real examination, the most difficult on earth, the test of familial expectations, like a long lost son who must be momentarily measured against a vision before he can be judged worthy of his spiritual patrimony. I wanted simply to say, "It's me," to thank him, sort of, for the guidance that he passed through three generations, and to assure him that I was fine in the way all Christian great-grandpas would want to know. I wanted to pass the test I only imagined him giving.

His wife, Neeltje, was there too. Each side of the stone featured a verse printed in Dutch beneath the names, places of birth and death, and two significant dates. It said "1836" beneath my great-grandfather's name, and a bit lower, "Gest. 1905."

It was then, when I saw the dates, that I began to understand "heritage." For C.C. Schaap's lasting gift to me has little to do with genetics, still less with ethnic pride, and nothing at all with nostalgia. What yet exists of this man, outside of the little his kin know of him, are the dates: 1836 and 1905, birth and death, his own lifetime. What he was, who he was, what he said, where he worked, what he made, who he knew, why he laughed, why he cried—all of that is gone now. And all that remains is a rather strange gravestone in Orange City, Iowa, a stone, a place that few of his descendants have visited since his death more than seventy years ago. Nothing else is left.

Someday—maybe soon, maybe not—I too will be placed somewhere to be so forgotten, just one of countless headstones on the earth which long ago the poet Bryant named but "one mighty sepulchre." Someday perhaps my great-grandchild will find it, looking, as I did, like some tourist on holiday. But his discovery will mean little if the lesson is somehow lost. I too must see how we all shall pass. And he must feel that what is important is not us, not what we do here, not who we impress, not how much we make. What is important, what is everything, is Him. For this, I know, is the real heritage of C.C. Schaap and his wife Neeltje and all such great-grandpas and great-grandmas already nameless for generations. What he has passed to me is the desire to believe and the legacy of a life aimed at worship. Through four generations his faith is alive and well, and during those moments when my new son opens his eyes to mine. I now know that I may not flout the birthright of C.C. Schaap, the blessed heritage of the covenant, a heritage that moves back through generations of names long since passed into obscurity and never stops, moving instead ever upward into the great promise of the great Father to such lowly progeny.

I'm just hoping that our friends in Washington feel something akin to what I felt then and still feel today. I'm hoping that both of our journeys lead us closer to home.

Buried Strangeness

Somewhere in the tiny cedar box which holds my mother's most treasured belongings, there is a three-by-five spiral notepad. On its blue cover, if I remember correctly, is the title, "The Lost Arrow Club." Inside that notebook, five or six pages tell the short history of a boyhood club to which I belonged. It's the proceedings of the club; but when I was eight years old, I knew nothing about articles or motions, so the proceedings amount to a disjointed narrative about a half-dozen sweatshirted boys who claimed allegiance to a scruffy organization headquartered in a backyard garden shed on the edge of town.

The proceedings explain how these boys would hike out to a deep gulch north of town, a fissure in the earth where some ancient river flowed east to the lake woods, and some blessed privacy for boys exploring themselves and the world. We called it—everybody did, nobody laughed—the Big Hole, and there wasn't much there but trees and water and an old dump—sometimes we'd save the farmer's empty Prince Albert tins because you can never tell when those little things come in handy. The notebook details the tragic loss of an arrow—all of two bits back then—how Davey Lensink was shooting the wooden 25-pounder his dad let him carry along on our expeditions, how he was shooting at a tree or a starling and how the arrow snuck into the meadow grass and escaped our feet and hands. Hence, the name, I imagine. In a ten-year-old's language that notebook explains how we followed the creeks and built huts from sod and felled tree

175

branches. The "proceedings" of the Lost Arrow Club glory in a treasured steel trap we hung like a prize from a nail hammered into a stud on the wall of the shack we met in, and it promises how muskrat and mink pelts will make all six of us rich enough to afford more arrows. There wasn't a one of us old enough yet for BB guns.

That notebook chronicles boyhood freedom in the middle of the tight protestant righteousness of a Dutch Calvinist village. That notebook symbolizes my own Tom Sawyer boyhood, the adventures growing like thin birch saplings from the woods and sand dunes of a childhood garden. Those two sources—the lake and the church—form the confluence from which my own identity has flowed.

The lakeshore I remember well. My mother said it was too dangerous for us to cross the busy highway that ran from Milwaukee to Green Bay, so we had to be old enough before we were allowed to escape the village for the woods and the lakeshore. At first we'd get off our bikes and walk across, scared silly of the cars and trucks with the strangers in sunglasses. But old enough and once across, we'd be in another world altogether. Entire days we'd spend in the woods, jerking down old logging shacks, plugging creeks like baseball-capped badgers, blowing wet hunks of rotten wood from upturned stumps with M-80s or cherry bombs we had hid for weeks up in our bedrooms. There was no real world around us at the lake; there were no teachers, no mothers, no playground supervisors to keep our language sweet or our zippers up. The lake was one vast unlined and unfenced playground.

Sometimes we'd find unimagined things in the ditches: pictures of naked women, remnant discards of a kind of passion we could feel but not name, and wine bottles with little in them but the smell of sin. For maybe three years I had been old enough to cross the highway, when one day we took along a rookie and found a skin magazine in glorious color.

"Women don't really look that way, do they?" he said. I remember how we laughed, because I remembered—and we all did—thinking the same thing ourselves once.

At ten years old one doesn't understand being poor, even if one is; neither does one understand the severity of righteousness. Growing up in a hall of mirrors allows no comparisons, and while today, in retrospect, it is easy for me to talk about the repression of Calvinism, a quarter century ago not one of the members of the "Lost Arrow Club" had any sense of the rigors of the tightly religious culture in which we grew. Every discarded bottle we found on our way to the lake simply smelled slightly like sin.

Growing up in a Dutch Calvinist conclave meant going through a litany of church activities which, at ten, we merely took for granted, because it never struck us that other people might not be running the same gauntlets. Weekly catechism, weekly Sunday School, devotions at every meal, twice-a-Sabbath worship—plus after-church hymn sings or missions reports—these constituted the altar of our lives. Some of us went to Christian schools, some did not. At age ten, few of us could understand the difference.

But it was a tight world. Few childhood songs ring through my memory as clearly as "Be careful little eyes what you see / . . . be careful little feet where you walk / . . . and be careful little hands what you touch." And I remember several people—teachers and uncles included—who insisted that Roman Catholics would not be seated next to the rest of us on Heavenly thrones someday. Dancing was wrong, drinking was skeptically tolerated in those who had not yet settled down to the easy chairs of home and family, and divorce was unpardonable. While the largely German-American towns that surrounded us celebrated themselves in summer rituals of bingo and booze, my own Dutch village, in its annual Fourth of July doings, never served beer and held a raffle that some good burghers (my own father included) wouldn't patronize. I will not forget my father's embarrassment, nor my own, when a relative took home one of the big prizes—maybe it was a concrete mixer.

When the Fourth of July landed on Saturday, village folks were caught in a conflict: empty popcorn boxes, silvery eskimo pie wrappers, and ketchupy napkins flecked the green park grass and turned that whole section of the village into an unholy mess. But no one dared to pick up on the Sabbath. Even cleanliness, in my Dutch Calvinist colony, was something less than godliness.

But no one needs to document the repressive nature of Calvinism. "Puritanism," said Mencken, "is the suspicion that someone, somewhere is having a good time." The caricature is deeply laid in our history, from the English roundheads, image-busters and theater-closers, to the American Puritans—Cotton Mather's devout writhing before the Lord, face down all day long in his closet. I grew up in a Calvinist world, but twentieth century Dutch Calvinists are not witch-hunting, stocks-slamming zealots, and life in a Dutch Calvinist town is not necessarily a death-in-life sentence.

Each childhood Christmas lives in my memory in rich sepiatones: the Christmas Eve Sunday School Program— complete with shepherds and angels and forgetful three-year-olds; a free brown bag of candy and peanuts and usually one orange for nutrition; the after-program ritual around the tree in our living room, always begun with a homily on the Greatest of Gifts—these memories live in me, for better or worse, as standards of family love and unity. Some of the heroes of my life were uneducated men whose strength and devotion and love spread over me like some unclimbable ageless pine on the ridge above the shoreline. My ethnic and religious inheritance includes a childhood of suffering the repression that always attends devout faith, a repression I knew nothing of when I was ten.

These two worlds, the open world of the lakeshore and the tight world of the village, shaped my life like a pair of sculptor's hands, so that even at ten I knew I lived in two worlds, one righteous—with all the concomitant blessings and curses of enforced righteousness—and the other free and natural, the buttercup world of spring in the lakeshore woods. And so I have always been conscious of two worlds, of being in but not of, of living in a religious sub-culture in the very center of Emersonian and American individualism. And that knowledge, that deep perception, colors everything I see even today.

The first short story I ever wrote concerns a boy who hears his Dutch Calvinist elders hold forth on the excesses of worldliness in the new country. An old man told me a story about two Dutch boys drowning on the Sabbath, about how that story tore up the town where they lived. Edgar Hartman, the main character of my story, feels the hell-fire passion of a patriarch in his father's blacksmith shop, hears the man claim that the preacher should be tougher on sin from the pulpit, hears him claim that through these deaths God himself is reproaching the whole town for such Sabbath desecration. A day or two later he goes to the farm of an American to bale hay and listens to the burly man claim the drowning was due only to the boys' negligence. The two versions of the story play off against each other in his mind—the excess of Calvinist allegory against the cold cause/effect sequence of the American. In one world heaven touches earth; in the other, there is no straight line up to God. Edgar eventually realizes that he is living in two worlds simultaneously, and he knows he cannot tight-rope between them forever.

Years later I tried a longer form than short fiction. By that time I felt confident in creating characters who would steer their own courses through the narrative, so I started with a missionary home on vacation after seven years of forgetting about the influence his own Dutch immigrant father had on his own values. By the end of the novella, the old man, broken by his wife's sudden death, asks his son for comfort for the first time his son can remember, and the missionary wavers between acceptance or rejection, not only of his father's need for compassion, but of his father's whole world, a world which includes the seven years he has spent bringing the Word as a missionary.

Recently, I wrote my first full-length play. I began with a story about an ex-actor who once spoke in tongues because he saw before him an audience, even if they were rural Kansas folk come to town for a revival. But the story shifted; by the end the plot had poured itself into what has become, for me, a familiar mold. A woman, who is running from her father and the many years she spent as musical prelude to her father's traveling salvation show, now feels his pursuit, long after she's rejected him and his faith. She is not drawn back to him when he finally confronts her, but she is somehow drawn to the image of her devout God-fearing mother, a woman more faithful to the calling of her belief than her flamboyant father. By the end of the play she makes peace with the faith of her childhood, settles for a compromise with the barnstorming legacy of a revival-hour salvation.

When I finished the play, and when I finished the novella, I was amazed at what had come from the pen. Certainly it is no secret that writers reveal something of themselves in everything they write, but the odd sentence of my Calvinist youth seems to be continual retelling of the same tale—characters who fight with the two worlds in opposition, then create new ways of making harmony.

Is this a prison? Is there no way to escape the birthright of separate cultures warring away within me, coming out time and time again in separate stories? Perhaps there is not. I think it was Willa Cather who claimed that every major theme a writer would ever use is embedded deeply within him or her by the time the writer is no more than eighteen years old. If my Calvinist upbringing hovers forever over my shoulder, it is perhaps no more unusual than the deep shadow of some other ethnic or geographic or religious past looming over anyone's present. We need not necessarily accept all the institutions of that tradition or birthright to live in peace with ourselves; we need only accept it as a life's presence, a given both in the writing process and the way we live—something Herman Melville, himself an inescapable Calvinist, apparently couldn't do, at least if we believe Nathaniel Hawthorne's evaluation of Melville—a man inordinately obsessed with finding God.

Years ago I came to treasure that Dutch Calvinist youth, even though it kept me from the mainstream American culture of the 1950s. I came to treasure it when I saw Emily Dickinson teasing a very familiar Calvinist god and sporting with the decaying Puritanism of 19th century Amherst, Massachusetts. I came to feel it in the way Thoreau thought about the ponds in *Walden*, in the theory of correspondences that underlies most every word Ralph Waldo Emerson ever wrote. That Calvinist past haunted me when I walked with Young Goodman Brown in Nathaniel Hawthorne's short story; and I felt it appear again in a man's obsession with a blemish birthmark. And it was there in Melville's white whale—the Jehovah God lovely enough to scatter white life in front of his chosen people, yet dangerous enough to challenge Abraham's love for his only and long-promised son. I knew that God, and I was, I discovered, specially chosen to understand some things about the whole gallery of American renaissance writers. This too was part of my legacy.

But all of that is American literary history, and in many ways my entire Oostburg boyhood is anachronism. Dutch Calvinism is to the New York literary scene what Oostburg, Wisconsin, is to the Las Vegas strip. My Calvinist sensibilities isolate me from the flow of American life as effectively as a small-town boyhood locks one up from the realities of racism, street violence, and West Coast glitter.

Nevertheless, as a writer, I can list at least three reasons why I rejoice in such an antiquated, parochial past and such an isolated, unique present. First, that old Dutch patriarch in my first story taught me that there is meaning in things—that God speaks in everyday life—even if too often we don't, or don't care to, understand clearly what he tells us. My Calvinist mind is given to romance, given to pursuit of meaning behind things, the pursuit, finally, of all writers. As Richard Chase says, "the Puritan [Calvinist] mind is given to allegory because it is sure of truth." The penchant for seeing allegory, for meaning in things, is both strength and weakness of the eyes I've inherited.

These lines I remember from the Chorus' summary preceding the third scene of Oedipus:

> Let each man take due earnings, then,
> And keep his hands from holy things,
> And from blasphemy stand apart—
> Else the crackling blast of heaven
> Blows on his head, and on his desperate heart.

181

Though fools will honor impious men,
In their cities no tragic poet sings.

The sturdy righteousness of my own ethnic culture, for-
tified by hours of family Bible reading, impressed me with
the desire to be the tragic poet—for better or worse, to
make some sense of a world displaced.

Second, living simultaneously in two cultures allows me
to view both with some objectivity. I never knew what it
meant to think like a Dutch Calvinist until I tried to think
in a different way. In a poem entitled, "A Hole in the
Floor" Richard Wilbur describes what he saw when staring
down through a hole at the joists beneath him. Suddenly,
he asks himself what it is he is doing:

> For God's sake, what am I after?
> Some treasure, or tiny garden?
> Or that untrodden place,
> The house's very soul,
> Where time has stored our footbeats
> And the long skein of our voices?
> Not these, but the buried strangeness
> Which nourishes the known:

The world beneath the floorboards complements the world
above. Having once perceived it, that new world affects
his vision:

> That spring from which the floor-lamp
> Drinks now a wider bloom,
> Inflaming the damask love-seat
> And the whole dangerous room.

A knowledge of two worlds alters our views of either.
Because of my Dutch Calvinist boyhood, I have the advan-
tage of double vision. "How lucky you are," a man once
told me, "to have two cultures to write from." Yes, I am.

Finally, I am reminded of something that the late John
Gardner, novelist and critic and scholar, said to me at the
Bread Loaf Writers' Conference in 1980. Gardner read a

story entitled "Come On Back," a story published in March of 1981 in *The Atlantic*. There is a passage from that story, and it doesn't matter if you don't know what's happening in the plot; I can start somewhere in the middle.

> Most of them seemed to have no need of the hymnbooks and couldn't have used them anyway, singing as they did with their heads lifted, mouths wide as fish mouths, proclaiming whatever it was they proclaimed not so much to the front of the hall as to the gleaming roof. They sang, as Welsh choruses always do, in numerous parts, each as clearly defined as cold, individual currents in a wide, bright river. There were no weak voices, though some, like Uncle Charley's, were reedy and harsh—not that it mattered; the river of sound could use it all. They sang as if the music were singing itself through them, moving like a current through a forest of seaweed—sang out boldly, no uncertainties or hesitations; and I, as if magic, sang with them, as sure of myself every note of the way as the wisest and heartiest in the room. Though I was astonished by my powers, I know, thinking back, that it was not as miraculous as I imagined. Borne along by those powerful voices, only a very good musician could have sung off key. It seemed as if all heaven and earth were singing, and when the music broke off on the final chord, the echo that rang on the walls around us was like a roaring AMEN.

Gardner read that story maybe a week into the conference. On successive nights I had heard the poet Linda Pasten, fiction writer Stanley Elkin, poets Marvin Bell and Nancy Williard, and others. But, that year, Gardner was the star of the conference, even though his story did not go over big—many thought it was boring. But it should be obvious that I loved hearing about the small-town Welsh in upstate New York, about their singing, about their oddities, about their hearts and souls.

So I saw Mr. Gardner afterward, leaning up against the wall of the building all the rest of us had just vacated. And I wanted to tell him how I felt, how his story made me feel suddenly legitimate.

"Mr. Gardner," I said. "I want to thank you for what you did for me with that story."

He smiled politely.

"You just made me feel free," I said. "I know that story —I mean, I'm not Welsh, but I know those people—those people are my people too."

"What's your name?" he said.

"Schaap—I'm Dutch—rural Midwestern Dutch—and I know those people."

He smiled.

"I just didn't know if I could write about my people the way you did. I mean, it's all these people from the city around here, you know—and I'm . . . well, their people aren't really my people. I'm from this provincial Dutch background—"

"Schaap," he said, "you and I are the lucky ones, aren't we?"

That *Atlantic* is still on the shelf above my desk.

Babel

Sure I'm Dutch, but I'm not dumb. I mean my father and my mother come here to this country with their families, but they been here for what now—close to twenty years already? And you know it is not so easy to go to town with them and have all the Americans hear them talk in that Dutch way. But they're learning. I try to teach them how to talk a little better, like the way they teach the little ones at Bakker School. I heard it when I was growing up.

"Don't twist your mouth so crazy," Miss Adkins would say to those that just come over. "You look like yer whistling, sweetie," she would say. "Just y-y-y-a-a-u-u-u, not e-e-e-e-u-u-u. That's no good way to talk." She would make them all do it together, I remember. "Keep that tongue down," she says to them. "Down, down, down—that's much better." She taught them all about this country. "This is America," she would say, real soft, "and you gotta learn to speak like the people in the land of freedom."

Anyway, I try to help my parents lose that brogue, you know, and when I think of it now, Pa isn't half so bad no more—why he can go right in the co-op and order feed just like he is really American. Ja, they know that he's Aaldert Hovenkamp, and he's immigrant and all, but they say nothing to him, eh? Not one thing. His language is coming now good finally. And I'll get him to say it right someday yet. But Ma, I don't know about. Ja, she don't get out that much, you know; not so much like Pa anyway. But I try to work with her too sometimes.

But I was saying though that I'm not dumb. And let me tell you, John Ledeboer is a stupid Hollander. I know it, and just about all of them in our church know it too. They all knew it sure the afternoon that he walked in the church with that army uniform, all straight and proud as if he was a hero or something, as if he really thought he was, eh? But everybody in town—Americans too—they all knew he could never be such a hero as he thought he was. The men down at the co-op, they knew it too. I just run in there on the Tuesday before he come in the church like that. They knew about Ledeboer coming back before his time. They ask me about him when I'm in the place: "Ledeboer comin' home already, Hovenkamp?" they says. "Weasel himself out somehow, right?" Ed O'Connor said it, but it's usually Ed what does most of the talking. So, what must I say to that? I knew that John *weasled* his way out somehow already the week before, and I was not proud at all of what he did. I wanted to say—I'll tell you what I wanted to say—I wanted to say, "Ja, the yellow bastard *weasled* out somehow." That's what I wanted to tell those Americans. But, ja—how can I say those things about Ledeboer? They knew I was a Hollander too—they knew where I go to church, on what side of town. They would laugh like little children if I would say such a thing about him. So I told them, "I don't think I know, O'Connor. I haven't seen him here yet on the street."

Now don't get me wrong. If my own father didn't have this farm here, I would have gone myself to Europe to fight that stupid heinie with these hands, I swear it. Sometimes I prayed that we should slaughter all of them Kaiser's men. Think once of what them Germans over there were doing to us here in Ireton. Ja, and what about the German people right here in town! Some Americans painted Hans Klug's livery with yellow paint just because someone heard Klug talk to a German customer in his own language. And not more than a week before that Sunday John Ledeboer came back, some of us came over from our side of town to see a fire right out in the middle of Main Street. And here they were, burning books, German books, and men like Klug and Heinrich almost crying right out there in front of everybody. Never before did I see such a thing, and the men crying like that too. So now you know what I have to feel about a man like Ledeboer—he runs away from his duty and laughs about it too. It didn't help things much—no, no, not much. And we knew right away that we would be suffering because *our* Ledeboer runs away.

Ach, even today this man Ledeboer makes me angry. He's a *slacker*, you know—a *slacker!* He just ran away; and he makes us all to suffer because of it. I ask you if that is right. Ja, so he was no citizen yet—what does that prove? He is in this country now, isn't he? The wooden shoes and all of that, it's back there, eh? When he comes to this country he should know that he was no more a Hollander—now, today, he is American. It means nothing not to be a citizen. What does that prove? You tell me! Well I know—nothing; it proves nothing at all. When you're here, you're here—that's all.

And I am not the only Hollander in Ireton who thinks that way either. I know many others who think this same way I do. Dirk Verstraate said it that afternoon in church, right out loud, so loud that everyone could hear him. "Ledeboer's a slacker," he says when John walks in. "He's nothing but a plain old slacker," he says. And we all agreed to that. After all some Hollanders are over there in Europe doing his fighting for him: there's Ed Douma and Henry Vander Kleed; and Fred Klooster will not return here, they say. So I feel nothing for a man like John Ledeboer. Ja, Dirk Verstraate is right—he is nothing but a slacker. For me, he deserved everything he got. He just makes it bad for all of us. I mean, what must we say to a man like Frank Fitzgerald, a good man, on the town council and such. Must I stand up for Ledeboer just because my parents come here from the same old country long ago? Nonsense. Nonsense. John Ledeboer is a yellow jackass, that's what I say, even to the men in the co-op. Someone like John Ledeboer puts us all in a, how would you say it?—a bad place, like my father would say, *"een kwaad daglicht."*

There we were, eh, sitting in the back row of the church, all the younger men, you know, where we always sit on Sunday afternoons. Anyway, we see this Ledeboer walk in

187

the church with his family, probably didn't even come to church in the morning. Anyway, here he comes in with that uniform all *netjes in de plooi,* cut straight and ironed sharp and right. And him just pulling all of that about not being really an American, just sneaking out of the army on some poor excuse while other good Americans are in France getting shot. Think of that once, will you? So we all sit up right away when we see him. Verstraate says, "Ledeboer's a slacker," and he says it right out loud. And Hank Vree sits up and whistles almost, like he does with his lips. The whole pew just shook like we were sitting on a porch swing all together side by side. The sermon hadn't started yet, so people was just beginning to come in the church.

And I want you to know that all of us Hollanders, everyone, to a man, thought it was stupid of him to wear that uniform after he had *weasled* out the way he did. If he wanted the glory for being in the army, then all of us said he should have stayed in corps like a man, and not wear that uniform as if he was a kind of hero. I swear to you, not a man in that church thought anything of John Ledeboer. We knew he was a coward, and a stupid coward too.

Well, those were the days of the language law, you remember? No I don't want to get into all of that business either. And I know that there was many people in our church, especially the older ones, who didn't think they were really worshipping the Lord with the English language. And we couldn't use the Dutch for the whole time of that law about other languages. I thought it was funny how there always had to be some American in our service, like we weren't really Americans at all, like we were really enemies of this free country. Opa said it was like that in the old country—somebody watching you all the time that way.

But I can see the point of the law too. This was war. We had to keep up some spirit here for the troops over there. We couldn't have German sympathizers here, we just couldn't. I heard once that Ed O'Connor called the Germans "baby killers" after that big ship went down, and

Fred Heinrich stood there next to him when he said it. And Fred's father still lives in the old country. Must have been very uncomfortable for a man like that. Ja, but I can see the point of the law too, you know? I can understand that.

I think it was Marvin Bishop or someone, I don't really remember who it was on duty in our church that afternoon. Sure we didn't use the Dutch; we were good law-abiding people and we listened to our governor. But we all knew that John Ledeboer would be in for it as soon as the word would get out. Ja, that's right. I'm sure now it was Marvin Bishop from the town council. I can remember the look on his face when he sees Ledeboer come in with the uniform on, the last one in a whole string of Ledeboers, John being the oldest. Sure, it was Marvin Bishop. He stood right in the corner, the far corner, away from the entrance. We all watched him, and he turned kind of red in the cheeks right then, I remember, because he knew for sure that everybody in the church was watching him too. We knew right away that John Ledeboer, the slacker, was in real trouble.

After church and supper we all met over at Van Daale's. Every Sunday night the young people would meet like that at somebody's house for some fun and such. Just our church, of course. Sometimes we'd read things or the Bible or something, but mostly we'd have fun. So that Sunday Ledeboer comes too—ja, he did, uniform and all. We hated him then. Even the girls hated him too because they knew what he was. Ann Van Daale didn't offer him even a bite to eat, not even a cookie or a cup of coffee. And he just sat in the corner there all by himself. He was thinking that we would come over to shake his hand or something foolish like that maybe, to tell him he was some kind of a hero.

But we didn't. He would get up and take a sandwich from the plate in the middle of the table, but we kept on talking as if no one was there even. Never looked up once. Anne never even gave him a cup, not one thing. It was kind of funny, really. After all, we were trying to keep him out, right? And he knew it—he had to know it, but he wouldn't just get up and walk away and leave us either.

He'd eat a cookie or something once in a while, as if he thought he was really one of us. We started to laugh about this crazy business after we finished eating. He was just kind of pushing us all the time, begging almost, and we wouldn't move either. Not one inch. I don't remember even what we talked about all that time, but everybody was thinking about John Ledeboer in that uniform. Must have been really uncomfortable for him, but he stayed right there.

And it wasn't more than an hour later when we heard those horns blowing outside the Van Daale's windows. No, I must say that there was nobody in that room that was all that surprised when they heard them. We all knew there would be something later on. He just went too far with that uniform. It wasn't long and they were right on the front porch, pounding on the walls of the house. "Bang, bang, bang," their fists beat on the walls and everything shook inside. And we were scared too, but we knew what they were after; it wasn't any of us either.

We stopped talking right away. We looked over at John for the first time. I guess he knew it too. I guess I can say it now, but for just one minute or so I felt some sorrow for him, because we all knew good what he was going to get from the Americans outside. But he deserved it too—and all of us were getting it too because of him being so stupid and a slacker.

First no one moved. He looked toward us with his eyes up, but his forehead was down like he was in prayer or something. He was peeking up somehow, like a naughty child. We all watched him very close now. We watched him raise his head like this and face us, straight on. It was a strange thing in that room—almost like there was something between us, but something apart too. I don't know how to describe it close really. I just felt funny for a little while.

The Americans beat on those walls and chanted something we couldn't understand so good. A blue and white dish from Holland fell right off the wall and smashed on the floor. Ledeboer gets up and walks out; he says nothing. He knows. He's not so foolish maybe—he knows what those Americans are after. So Dirk Verstraate says, "Good riddance!" when Ledeboer leaves. "Good riddance!" he says, and he closes the door behind Ledeboer. "Just a slacker," he says. We all agreed.

They stopped that chanting almost right away. We ran to the window. By the time we looked Ledeboer had on no clothes but his underwear. They carried him up on their shoulders like he was some kind of animal. A woman folded up his uniform like it belonged to her son. They carried him down to the road there in front of the house. Then there were torches all over and a big fire in the road. We stepped outside on the front step. I smelled kerosene and liquor.

And they were beating on him. We watched them—all of us. We hated that guy too, you know, and we just hated to be there then. He was really stupid for wearing that uniform. The moment he walked into the church we knew that something would happen to him for sure. Ja, it was so stupid of him. And he was a slacker on top of it all.

We didn't talk much, just watched. But before we knew it, they were all around us too—the Americans. There was some there we knew from town, softball players; we went to school with them in the years before.

We didn't try to fight them. And when I felt them pushing me and saw the others going too, I was sure that we were all going to be beaten because of John Ledeboer. We went one at a time, in a line toward the road—Hank, then me, then Dirk, and the others. We were pushed along by people from town. To the middle of the street. We saw him there lying on the gravel.

"Kick him Hollander!" They were all yelling and chanting.

I could just see Ledeboer there between the legs of all the people. They took first Hank and pushed him up toward the middle. The torches made the air very warm.

"Kick him you damn Dutchman!"

Two of them had me by the arm. I did not dare to try to pull myself free. We were all surrounded, you see. Then I saw Vree's head go down in a jerk. I didn't see him kick, but I know he followed their orders.

191

"Harder! Kick him 'till he groans!" It was Ed O'Connor again.

They pushed me up closer to where I could see Ledeboer lying on his back. He was bloody. It ran from his nose and his mouth, and down his face and into his blonde hair where it stuck in clumps.

And then I heard a thud, like a soft melon falling on the road from the back of a flatbed wagon. And I saw Hank himself buckle when somebody slammed a fist into his belly.

"Get up there, Hovenkamp. You're next?" they said.

I saw that John's eyes were half shut. He seemed nearly dead, but he wasn't. And he was plain naked. Don't remember ever seeing such a stark naked man before right out there in the street. And then I tried to think about him strutting into the church in that uniform and weasling out of the war. And I tried to think about Fred Klooster—they were saying that he would never come back to the farm. I remembered Dirk saying that Ledeboer wasn't nothing but a lousy slacker.

"Kick him," O'Connor says.

And I guess it's like I just don't remember at all what happened there just then. I don't think I kicked him, but the next thing I know is I was on the gravel sitting next to Hank, watching Dirk, who was next in line.

Well, I guess them Americans thought that this kicking wasn't quite enough. O'Connor and somebody else picked up Ledeboer, one on each arm. His head flopped like it was loose from his shoulders, just kind of dangled there. His knees were useless, his legs split out beneath him. He was stark naked.

"Hit him!" they yelled. "Hit him!"

"Where?" Dirk says.

"In the face."

Ledeboer was coughing a little, then heaving just like a little baby. Dirk watched him. They shoved at Verstraate, as if they couldn't waste any time. "Hit him!" they said again, together. Dirk took off his jacket and the crowd cheered. When he rolled up his sleeve, they all yelled out that Ledeboer was nothing but a slacker. Dirk leaned back and took a big breath and threw a right as hard as he could, yelling loud, like he was swinging a sledge, and his fist caught Ed O'Connor flat against the side of the head. I swear Ed's head turned completely around on his shoulders like a bird's might. It sounded flat, like a bullet hitting an oak.

Well, that was it, of course. We all got beat up then for sure. Finally the law showed up and broke the fight up. But you know, Dirk broke Ed's jaw like it was made a glass.

And that was two years ago. Ed still works in the co-op and he talks as much as ever, but he never mentions that Sunday night during the war. Ledeboer's got some land of his own already—my mother says, *"Hij is met z'n gat in de boter gevallen,"*—and he's married some school teacher from Wisconsin. Dirk moved to Sioux City after the war. Works in the stockyards downtown. Never see him any more again.

And Ireton lost two in the Great War. One American, one Hollander. Now our church uses the Dutch language again. Nobody cares too much anymore, at least there never is any Americans in our church to listen. My mother likes it; for almost a year she sat and read from her *Psalter.* But I'm against it, and there's others of us too, younger ones. Seems to me we should be learning this new language here in America.

Revival Fires

Henry Witten rather respected his future father-in-law, not only because he was Lillian's father, but also because he was, for a preacher, quite a reasonable man. Henry had determined that if he were to join a church in later years—once he graduated from the University—he would likely become a member where a man like Reverend Ten Clay was the pastor, some thoughtful, unassuming, and more than intermittently perceptive man. On occasional Sundays Henry admitted to himself that he had even learned things from Ten Clay's sermons; he assumed that the acquisition of some worthwhile insight was as much as you could ask from any church.

Reverend Ten Clay himself asked Henry over for dinner the first Sunday he was home from the University. The preacher sat there with a forkful of roast pork, the rest of the family quietly waiting for him to speak once grace had been said. It was obvious that all of them had cut their behavior from the Sunday-best standards, even Andrew, the only boy, the adopted, dark-haired Ten Clay.

"Lillian's mother and I want you to come along to Lake Windsor with us this June, Henry. We think that since you're going to be part of this family, it may be a good opportunity for us to get to know you better—and you, us." It seemed a reasonable request, even if religious revival was hardly Henry's taste in vacations.

But Henry Witten was, after all, quite perceptive. He knew what the actual motivation was the moment the preacher asked, and he didn't need Lillian to tell him later.

"You know the reason he asked you to come along, don't you?" she said, when her little sisters and her adolescent brother, Andrew, were cleaning up after the meal, and the preacher was in his study preparing for the afternoon service.

"He wants to test you a little—to see what you think of spiritual things like the Conference." She made it sound as if it were some quaint test of honor. She wound her arm around his waist, tucking her shoulder beneath his. "My father the preacher doesn't want his daughter marrying a heretic," she whispered. And then she kissed him on the cheek, like a loving mother might kiss her daughter on the first day of school.

"I'm going on trial, I suppose," he said. "Some kind of Presbyterian Inquisition." He stared up at the ceiling.

"Don't be so thin-skinned. You know our family goes down there every year—ever since the end of the War." Lillian straightened his collar a bit. It was the way she did it that bothered him, straightening it as if they were about to have a family portrait taken. "Besides, you know he means well."

"Whose side are you on?" Henry said. He looked out through the window at the side door of the old church as he crossed his legs. "Hitler meant well, you know." He knew right away by her silence that he shouldn't have said it, but Henry had been raised Presbyterian, had learned the Westminster Catechism with Lillian's father. Obviously, all of that wasn't sufficient proof of his orthodoxy. That's what angered him.

And the cause, he knew, was the University. Three years he had at the University, and Henry knew that to Ten Clay, and most of the small town in which he had been reared as a child, learning itself was somehow suspect. Furthermore, he was sure that the entire exercise was being undertaken to determine the validity of one absurd thesis: that somehow learning didn't effect any change in the individual—especially with respect to faith. It made him angry to think that such a notion could reside in the mind of his future father-in-law. Reverend Ten Clay was, after all, quite a reasonable man, even from the pulpit. Henry had long ago thought it through clearly: if learning wasn't affective, then one would be hard pressed to say that any significant learning had ever gone on. Of course there would be change. That seemed clear to him. What nature of learning could have taken place when no significant change was apparent in the individual?—when there were no demonstrable results? What was learning, after all, but change?

Henry Witten appreciated the sound of rhetorical questions.

Three weeks later they left. Reverend Ten Clay put Lillian and himself and the two girls in the back seat, pointed Andrew to the front between himself and his wife, then took the wheel of the '39 Chevy, and drove south past the state line towards Lake Windsor, the Baptist Conference Grounds, two full bags of sandwiches and a dozen apples tucked in the back window.

Up front, Andrew, the dark-haired Ten Clay, sat jammed between his mom and dad; he seemed determined not to sway in either direction, unwilling to suffer slightest touch from either parental shoulder. Not once did the boy speak.

"Do you want a sandwich, Andrew?" his mother would say, and the boy would emit some ape-like grunt that only a mother could translate, as if the whole business were an affront to his dignity. Henry thought maybe such a kid had some redeemable attributes. Obviously the Conference meant as much to Andrew as it did to him. Henry thought he should make a point of getting to meet the kid a little better. At least they shared an attitude, he thought.

"We're down for two rooms this year," the preacher told the boy at the front desk of the boarding house, "one for the men and one for the women."

"Kick-off is coming up in less than an hour," the boy said. "Pastor Angus Stillwell all the way from Wilkes-Barre. Ever hear him?" The boy looked up at Henry as if Henry himself were some circuit revivalist.

"No, I'm sorry I haven't," Henry said. "I'm sure he'll do

197

just fine." Henry felt as if he were accepting advice on salad dressing from some waitress in some good restaurant.

"The man's a real fireball for Jesus," the boy said.

Maybe it was the boy's thick, red cheeks Henry disliked, or the fact that he was overweight—saggy rolls of fat threatened to gush from the red shirt girdling his waist. Maybe it was the bowl-on-the-head, Okie haircut, like some freshman from the farm. Maybe it was that sanctimonious smile.

"We better get ourselves moved in before the fireball really lights things up." Reverend Ten Clay smirked noticeably when he said it, Henry thought, a comforting kind of supercilious Presbyterian elitism, as if to tell Henry that not all of the shallow emotional gush had to be accepted uncritically.

"You help the women, Henry. I'll try to keep a hold of Andrew here." The heavy-set kid handed Henry one of the keys, chained to a laminated wooden cross—"Tyler's Rooms, Lake Windsor," on one side, and some verse from scripture on the other.

"I've got John 3:16 here, Henry. How about you?" the preacher said.

"That's all we got is 'For God so loved the world,'" the boy said, picking up the fly swatter from the desk top.

The whole business was priceless, Henry thought. When he turned away from the desk, he saw Andrew, his thumbs curled in his front pockets, slumped against the wall near the door.

Spurgeon Assembly Hall was an impressive frame structure with a classical facade complete with Corinthian pillars, but the sanctuary itself was low-ceilinged, so low that when the song-leader ascended the platform, the sinners in the rear craned their necks to see him up there. Henry thought the Ten Clays and the other late-comers in the back looked like penned geese, the way their heads swayed to catch a glimpse of the man.

Henry was, of course, woefully out of place from the onset, from the first of the Christian battle songs to the last droning mood-maker—something about a "sweet, sweet feeling"—sung a cappella, of course, a typical low-church approach to liturgy, he thought, an overture to the emotional swell so essential to revivalism. A year ago he had taken a course in American history—studied the Great Awakening in depth: itinerant preachers, religious enthusiasms, and even Jonathan Edwards, the last of the American Calvinists. Revivalism, he knew, had a long and occasionally colorful history.

Lillian sat next to him, squeezing his hand as if to prevent him from spontaneously speaking in tongues. And Andrew, who absolutely insisted on sitting at the end of the row, fidgeted, for the most part, to Henry's right, always keeping his head down, his hands on his chin, back slumped away from the wooden folding chair.

It took only a song or two for the huge song leader—a straight-cut tall man in suspenders—to prompt the requisite responses: the Amens and Praise the Lords and the other stock phrases the assembly inserted in thick, deep breaths for end punctuation. By the time Pastor Stillwell arose, the song leader had them warmed and loose, perfectly primed and responsive, a textbook case in mob manipulation. Experiencing such a thing was like being some avid scholar able to wallow in the recently uncovered bounty of a lost civilization.

The fact is, he never saw Andrew leave. The boy must have leaned off his chair and simply walked out. No one missed him at first, and when Henry finally did take note of the kid's absence, he simply assumed it was nature calling. But Pastor Stillwell was bullying up for the final assault when Henry decided that no trip to the facilities should take as long as Andrew's absence had lasted. So he told Lillian.

"Where did he go?" she said.

The whole business had filled him with sarcasm. "Am I my brother's keeper?" he said.

Pastor Stillwell had the assembly throbbing. Directly in front of them a small man in a flowered shirt was on his feet, babbling, his short-sleeved arms in the air, palms up. Lillian had to speak out loud to make herself heard amid the jubilation.

"Go on," she said. "Go out and look for him."

"Where?" he said.

She shook her head and squinted, put her hand to her ear.

"I said, 'Where?'" he repeated, almost yelling.

"Let's get out of here," she said.

He wasn't about to argue. Each firm step up the aisle and away from the crowd thrilled him. He pushed through streams of people flowing down to answer the preacher's call. There was, he thought, a kind of righteousness in walking in the opposite direction. All around him, ugly people—men in straw hats, women in hair nets with children blindly following, their faces awash in smiles and tears—all around him folks swarmed up toward Pastor Angus Stillwell to herald the new testimony of their faith, as if tonight's kick-off were some Damascus road event, their first big bite of gospel truth. Who but a believer would come to a place like this in the first place, he asked himself, walking tall against the grain, Lillian behind him.

"Did he say anything?" she said when they made it out. "Where did he go?"

Escaping the irrational made him think of Andrew as a kind of saint. "Maybe he's up front repenting," Henry told her.

He meant it as a joke but she didn't take it that way. "He's done it before," she said. "I never wrote you about it—my father doesn't like to admit it himself."

"What do you mean?"

"Andrew. He's run away before."

"Run away?" he said.

Lillian took his arm at the elbow. He felt her hand on him almost like a reprimand. "We've got to find him before he gets away too far. You know your way back to the boarding house?"

"Of course," he said.

"Go back there right away. Andrew knows his way around. I'll look at the lakefront—by the shops."

"Lillian," he said, "will you tell me what's going on?"

"Andrew's done it before," she said, "run away like this.

We've got to find him before my parents find out—it just kills them when he does it. Go on, Henry," she said. She left him there beneath the pillars. "Go!" she yelled.

He half-trotted down the lamp-lit street, on lookout for a kid whose figure he remembered only vaguely. Andrew never was a favorite of his. When he started seeing Lillian, the boy was just beginning the rebellious stage, and Andrew was a typical adolescent—moody, self-indulgent, contrary, an ogre with acne. Henry had no vivid desire to find him, much less to speak to him. But he watched the sidewalks around him and the windows, yellow squares of light in the march of boarding houses adjacent to the Conference grounds. Perspiration formed beneath his stiff collar.

"Andrew," he yelled. But he thought it would be foolish to yell. If the kid wanted to run away he certainly wouldn't respond.

He turned down the side street and headed toward the rooms the Ten Clays had rented. And then he saw the old Chevy coming up the street. He was sure there weren't two Chevys like that in all of Lake Windsor, and when it came closer he saw the yellow out-of-state plates.

"Andrew," he yelled. It was too dark to see the driver, but he was positive it was the Chevy. He ran into the road when he heard the car shift into second. "Andrew," he yelled.

The Chevy seemed to draw a bead on him. He moved back toward the curb, just a step, but the old thing kept coming at him, like some wounded animal.

"Andrew," he yelled again, but the car held its course.

Fear locked his lungs so he couldn't yell, but the Chevy kept coming.

"Andrew, what on earth—" He mumbled it to himself, his eyes fixed on the grill and the windshield, two plates of dark glass like a mask.

At the last second he jumped away from the car and toward the sidewalk, and he felt the brush of air when the old Chevy swept past him, its tire grazing the curb just hard enough to wedge off a half-dollar wheel cap and send it on a roll down the sidewalk.

Humiliation sent him sprinting after the car. The idea of some mindless adolescent threatening his life was a shocking personal affront. When he saw the outlines of a crowd moving against the white assembly hall, he knew Andrew would be forced to slow down at the intersection or risk carnage, blood gushing from redeemed bodies, children bouncing off the preacher's car and flopping to the cement like old mattresses. Ten Clay's preacherly face, drawn and beaten, hung from his imagination.

When he saw the weak brake lights flash, he ran ever faster, confident he could catch the car. Andrew turned right at the corner and headed out of town slowly, through the mob streaming from the hall. Henry cut through front lawns and what seemed hundreds of people, catching up just past the intersection. He jumped on the running board, his hands grabbing the half-opened window on the passenger side.

"Andrew, for Pete's sake, stop this thing," he said, not unconscious of the spectacle being created. But there was no response. "Andrew, what you trying to do—kill me?"

Andrew never looked up. "Let go!" he said. "Let go!"

"You're crazy—you know that? This is downright crazy," Henry yelled. He figured they must have been up to forty. "Stop the car!" He reached for the inside door handle with his right hand, but instinct told him it was safer to hold on than to jerk the big door open over the running board. "Andrew, stop this car!" he yelled. But Andrew kept accelerating.

The light of the street lamps withdrew as they moved out into the woods, the car weaving in and out through the curves around the lakeshore. Bugs and moths rapped against his face and body. Wind pushed his face into distortion.

"Andrew," he yelled. "What are you doing?"

But there was no reply. He could see the boy's face in the dim glare of the dash lights, sitting up close to the wheel, both his hands clinging to the top.

Somehow, even in his imagination, he would never have guessed he could be in such an insane position. The thought flickered in his mind—this had to be imagined somehow.

But the kid said nothing.

The wind pushed back his hair and forced tears from the corners of his eyes. He felt himself squinting, clinging to the door, jerking his body around when beetles smashed up against his chest like slugs or grazed off his head. Yet, somehow it struck him as insane, as silly—him hanging to the side of some old Chevy, as if he were some gangster, some Chicago-land enforcer, his scalp bared to the wind, willing to risk it all to get his man. It had an absurdist quality to it, the whole insane business.

"You tryin' to kill me?" he said.

"I didn't ask you to come along," the boy yelled.

"I'm not ready to die! If you don't want murder on your hands, you better stop this thing!"

Andrew's chin pointed forward, his eyes squinting as if he were trying to peer through some deep fog.

"You hear me, Andrew?" he yelled.

Warm gusts hit him like hot breaths. Moisture stuck in his hair, formed like dew against his cheeks.

The boy looked at him just for a second, a mean look, his lips jerked up beneath his nose.

"One thing to run away, but murder's something else altogether—"

That was the right thing to say. He felt the wind die suddenly, as if they had entered the eye of a hurricane. The Chevy's roar cut back to nothing. Slowly they came to a stop, the car pulling up close to the fieldstone fence along the side of the road. His arms loosened and dropped from the window, and his face pricked and burned in the sudden stillness.

"He ain't my father," the boy said. "And she ain't my mother either. You know that."

Henry opened the door from the inside and swung his body in. With his right hand he pulled back his hair, and he spit out the bugs through the open window. "My God," he said, "right out of Al Capone."

"You know he ain't my father," the kid said.

"Where'd you get the key anyway?" Henry said.

"I don't need no key."

Henry wished it were a marketable skill.

"He always lets it in the trunk like a fool. Besides, I don't need a key."

"How much money you have?" Henry said.

Andrew hunched his shoulders.

"Well, aren't you a wonder? Just exactly how far you assume a kid—how old are you anyway?"

"Sixteen."

"How far a sixteen-year-old kid with no money, driving an old wreck Chevy with out-of-state plates—how far you think you'd get?" Henry purposely stared at the boy.

"Don't matter. He ain't my father—that's all that matters. Running away is what matters—that's all."

"Got gas enough?"

"Quarter tank."

"That right?"

"Go a long way on a quarter tank."

"All the way to Las Vegas." Henry hated adolescents even when he was one himself. Here he was in the middle of a family crisis he knew nothing about, alone with a sickening rebel kid he rabidly disliked, at the brink of an argument he was, at best, indifferent to, and on top of everything, he was angry, still pulling bugs out of his hair.

That Andrew was no Ten Clay seemed perfectly obvious. His hair was deep brown and thick, so low on his forehead it seemed almost to threaten his eyes. His hairline pointed down into two wedges and bordered a square forehead no larger than a belt buckle. His eyes were dark, nearly always downcast and forever sullen, an attribute Henry had before blamed on a terminal case of puberty.

"What you going to do?" the kid asked.

"What do you mean by that? It would appear to me that it's you who has to do something now. After all, it's not my flight that drew us together here in the middle of nowhere."

"Why don't you talk plain," Andrew said. "You ain't at college now." He laid his hand over the top of the wheel like an experienced driver. "And I ain't impressed anyway." He flicked a thumb at Henry. "You going to get out or what?"

"It's next to ridiculous to think—"

"What?"

Henry wondered if a square forehead was a sign of mental retardation. "No," he said, "I'm not leaving."

Andrew took a cigarette from his jacket pocket.

"You smoke?" Henry said.

"The butt does."

"Clever," he said.

The Chevy was still running, its idle choppy and irregular, shaking the car as if it were barreling down the road.

"It stands to reason that there's nothing to be gained by this stunt, you know?" Henry said.

"He ain't my father."

"You've already clearly established that fact, Andrew. Would you listen to reason? Whether or not you come back with me, you'll end up back there soon. You're no adult, you've got no more gas, and you're driving a marked car. You'll be lucky, really lucky, if you make it till dawn. That's a plain and simple fact, Andrew. Will you use the head the Lord gave you?"

"He ain't my father."

"What is it—some kind of obsession with you?" Henry inhaled deeply. Irrational acts began to appear to him quite plausible. He could make a stab for the keys—but then Andrew already said he didn't need them. He could knock the boy silly with his fists. He could drive him down the road and let him off somewhere, get him forever lost.

He settled on mock compliance. "I'm not about to walk back now," he said. "You might as well consider me a kind of sidekick on this blasted frolic of yours."

The kid didn't understand. It was written in his face, the way he squinted. "I'm coming along," he said, as if he were speaking to someone half-deaf—"do you understand?"

Andrew flicked the butt out the window.

They stopped at a roadhouse tavern, not more than ten miles from Lake Windsor, as close as Henry could guess. He wasn't excited about taking an adolescent into some seedy country saloon, but their ever-increasing distance from the Conference grounds prompted him to offer Andrew something to eat in hopes of slowing things down. "I'll buy," he said. Henry thought his choice of words entirely appropriate.

"This here's a place to drink," Andrew said.

He wanted to compliment the boy on his powers of observation, but he restrained himself.

The four or five men at the bar obviously hadn't made the big Kick-off at the Conference. They all half-turned on their stools when Andrew and Henry walked in, then watched them closely, in the manner of a graduate biologist.

Andrew walked past them with born-again resolve and took a stool at the end of the bar, the woman right there to serve them the moment they sat down.

"What'll it be?" she said. It was obvious she thought of them as peers. Henry decided that she would have made Andrew the kind of mother he deserved.

"Do you have anything to eat?" he said.

"Got some sausage here."

"That's all?"

"Cut you any size hunk you like."

Andrew suddenly had another cigarette between his fingers.

"Okay, bring on the sausage," he said.

"And something to drink?"

"Two glasses," Andrew said, and she was gone before Henry could stop her.

She wore a kitchen smock like some country grandma; her arms, spotted with black and blue marks, were thick as whitewalls. She came back with two glasses in one hand and a tube of sausage with a long kitchen knife in the other.

"I don't suppose you have any scotch?" Henry said.

"We don't sell no liquor here—just beer." She drew the knife up along the tube. "Just tell me when."

"Good. Right there," Henry said.

The knife sliced through the meat in one long pull.

"More?" she said. She was the kind of woman Henry felt embarrassed to have to look at.

"No thanks," he said.

"Dime for the beer. Nickel for the sausage," she told him. She pushed the point of the blade through the skin on the meat, then stripped it with her fingers.

Henry pushed a quarter toward her.

That's when the cops came in through the front door.

"We usually find them that run off at one of the saloons, especially when they take off from the Conference Grounds—you know what I'm saying?" The officer explained things as if there were nothing new under the sun. "It's a reasonable thing. Them kids get rebellious when they get sat on—you know, all that Bible stuff. Happens all the time, Reverend. You shouldn't be thinking that something like this is all that unusual. Happens more often than these people here like to admit." The man had a way of scratching his belly when he talked, as if he were home in the shower. "Shoot, it's a natural thing for a kid like him to have a wild streak." He slapped Andrew's shoulder, maybe a bit too hard, Henry thought.

Lillian smiled politely and told the officer they wouldn't be needing him anymore.

"You going to stay put now, kid?" The man took hold of his arm. "It's a heckuva world out there, take it from me. I wouldn't want to be throwing no preacher's kid in a tank full of drunks." Andrew stared at the man's hand. "You listen to the preacher now—he's your old man."

They had drawn quite a crowd when they pulled up, the burly officer escorting Andrew in, the boy's hands tied behind his back. Henry thought it was overdone and a bit theatrical, especially the way the sergeant kept the red lights flashing all the while he roared around in the front room of the boarding house.

Lillian's mother sat crying in the corner of the lobby, one of her little daughters already asleep on her lap. Behind her the big wall clock ticked out the seconds.

The odd thing about it was the fact that, considering the breadth of all that had happened, it still wasn't very late. By the time Henry had followed the squad car up to the boarding house, it was just a short prayer past eleven, the whole business begun and concluded in less than two hours.

"Something we can do beside pray?" the kid with the Okie haircut said.

Henry looked at the boy's eyes and cheeks and hair, but he didn't answer the question. There were faces all around gaping through the windows, plastered to the screen door.

"Let's go to bed," the preacher said.

The door slapped shut behind the officer.

"I can't sleep in that room with him, Henry," the preacher said. His eyes were cut and glassy from the moisture that threatened, but he tried to hold a smile. He worked at it. "My wife needs me, but the fact is that I just can't bring myself to face him now." It was the same face Henry had seen in his mind the moment Lillian told him that Andrew had run off before. And Henry knew it was the preacher's lot to suffer like he was. It was his character. A sterner man would have written off the adopted son on the basis of bad genes. A weaker man could have succumbed to the release of emotional collapse.

"It's not that I don't love him, Henry. You've got to understand that," he said. "And it's not that I haven't tried." His lips tightened. "God knows what we've tried to do for that boy. You think we haven't tried, Henry?" he said.

"No, sir."

"Lillian knows we've tried." He looked away, down the hardwood floor hallway, then down and into his clean hands. "But I can't be with him again just now—I can't face him anymore tonight. You understand? Maybe tomorrow I'll take him down to the lake—rent a boat—I don't know—try again. But not anymore tonight. Not anymore." He drew his hand down slowly over his face, then held it over his mouth, his eyes drawn.

"He'll be all right now, Reverend Ten Clay. I'm sure it's just a stage—"

The preacher turned away, down the hall to the other family room. "It's like Absalom, Henry. It's Absalom I remember. Your mind does crazy things. How often I've thought that both of their names begin with A. That's what your head does."

A full-grown man hung from his hair in a tree, swaying with the chant of his father's grief in the Psalms.

"You try, Henry. Maybe you can do something for the boy. Lillian's mother and I—" He shook his head.

The glass knob squeaked when he turned it. "If you could count the prayers—" he said.

"I'm sure, sir," he said. "I know you have."

"I don't think you know, Henry. You've never been a father." The persistent smile stayed in place. He laughed, slightly, looked away as if he were embarrassed, then looked back at Henry and laughed again. "And Henry," he said, "we had no time to talk, but what do you think of the fireball?" He waited for no reply. "It's good for me to hear them, you know—that's what I think. Good for me. That's why I come down every year like this, good old Presbyterian like me."

The door closed softly behind him.

The dim light coming through the open window outlined Andrew's body against the sheets. Outside, the resort village was quiet, its fervor settled in the damp evening air. The lamps still spread a soft yellow radiance over the streets, but no one moved anywhere near the camp, the gray sidewalks empty. Henry watched the silence from the window.

For the life of him, he couldn't figure how Lake Windsor could be good for the preacher.

"You sleeping, Andrew?" he said, still looking out the window.

He didn't expect a response.

It was some time before he could fall asleep himself.

He awoke when Andrew sat up in bed, but he made no move to stop the boy, hoping that Andrew simply needed the restroom down the hall. But when he stepped from the bed fully clothed, Henry knew it was happening again, and he felt himself shoved into a commitment that was sealed by the despair on the preacher's face. Maybe this was the test, he told himself, something the preacher himself never planned.

Andrew tiptoed across the floor and twisted the knob with a slow turn that muted the metallic shrieks. Henry turned his head slowly without moving his body. The moment Andrew was out of the door, Henry reached for his pants. He put on his shoes without socks, jammed his arms into his shirt, buttoned it, and poked his face into the hallway. Andrew was already gone. He moved slowly down the hall, not wanting the boy to panic if he heard footsteps behind him.

He felt for the key to the Chevy in his pocket and he found it there, but he walked around the back of the place anyway, sure that Andrew would start for the car again. He found him leaning over the engine, the hood up. He walked up quietly behind him.

"Can't you see it's insane, Andrew?" he said.

The boy twisted around, his eyes flashing and he swung his fist. In the time between Henry's first glimpse of it and the crunching sound it made against his jaw, his mind registered a thousand different things he might have said. But Andrew connected with the fist. Henry had time enough only to fade with the flow, so the fist did not catch him full force, but with just enough impact to send him staggering back into a bush, arms spread, like a fighter rebounding off the ropes. He tasted blood immediately.

In the twisting world in his head, Henry knew little except that Andrew was running. The boy's feet crackled the loose gravel down the driveway. Henry sat for a second on one knee, then rose slowly, wiping his face with his sleeve. Blood streaked the white cuff. He shook his head, trying to regain his balance, then brought both hands up to his forehead to try to stop the shaking inside. Andrew, he knew, was gone again.

Henry ran to the end of the alley, his legs soft as sponge beneath him. He looked both ways down the street, but he saw no moving legs, nothing to break the still darkness. The old Chevy would be his only chance; Andrew would surely not stay in the village. He ran back to the car, his legs still shaky, his eyes focusing more clearly, the doubled images fusing only when he concentrated his vision.

He fumbled for the keys, turned them in, kicked the ignition, and the Chevy rumbled once and then started.

The streets were dead. The darkened rooming houses stood one after another in a parade of silence, the believers final amens spent hours ago. The sturdy cop reappeared in his mind, but the man was a county officer, he remembered, and he could be anywhere. When he saw his lights illumine the big pillars of the Assembly Hall, he realized he was alone with Andrew. If the boy were to be saved, it would be, even to the boy's father, the work of Henry Witten.

He shut off his lights, the thought of the stupid kid against him firming his resolve. Once Andrew had tried to run him down. Blood still trickled from the corner of his lips where the ungrateful kid—the rebellious, adopted kid—had assaulted him with one violent clenched fist. Reason be hanged, he told himself. He would run the jackel down himself if it took him till morning.

He jerked the car into first at the Assembly Hall corner and turned right, guessing the kid would fly out on the road he had taken before. He tried to estimate how long it had been—four, five minutes—since Andrew had hit him, then guessed how far an adolescent could sprint in that time. The Chevy poked along in first, jerking when he'd let up even a bit on the gas. He looked for any sign of movement, a shaking hedge, the flash of a white sock, maybe a light on where some Baptist heard someone moving outside. The broad oaks that lined the street barely moved. There was no wind.

And there was little gas, the needle pointing almost directly at the E. Little gas meant little time. He left the village and started winding down the lakeshore road. The moon shown nearly full, the sky clear, the road an almost bright gray against the woods, the fieldstone fence clearly visible at the edge of the pavement. He shifted slowly into second, hoping the old Chevy would quiet down in a higher gear. He stayed in second through the turns, his eyes focused more clearly now, sweeping both sides of the road.

He shifted into third and went north another half mile,

211

wondering if he had already gone too far. And then he saw movement. It may well have been a deer, but something jumped the stone fence on the right side of the road. Rather than stop, he drove past as if he had seen nothing, guessing he could at the very least out-think the kid with the square forehead.

He kept moving up the road, far enough through the curves so he was sure that Andrew wouldn't see him quickly. He would go back past the spot where he had seen the movement, lights on, yelling out the kid's name, knowing full well the boy wouldn't respond, guessing Andrew would think, once he had passed him again, that the chase was over for the time being. Then he'd circle back, lights on, as if he were just any other car. Come down full speed—as if he weren't looking for anyone at all. Andrew wouldn't think it was him—not until he could see the car against the glare of headlights. Maybe by then he'd be close enough to catch the kid on foot.

He congratulated himself on his genious. It was his best chance. He had intelligence on the kid, that much he knew.

Still in second, he commenced yelling from the window.

"Andrew, this is it, your last chance! Andrew, come out. I know you're in there. Andrew! Andrew! Andrew, come on back with me—I won't tell your father. Andrew! Andrew!"

On both sides of the road the woods stood perfectly still, tall and black and dead. The lake's warmth drifted up in a slow mist that hung above the road in scattered spots like thin clouds dropped purposely to earth. Andrew wouldn't appear.

When he came back to the Hall, he turned right, then turned around to face the big pillars. He killed the engine and waited. He checked his watch, but his eyes still flashed a fuzzy double image. Blinking, pulling the watch up close to his eyes and aiming the face at a street lamp, he could barely make out the minute hand. It was already after three in the morning. He would wait ten minutes at least. Andrew could probably get another mile down the road in that time; he would never guess it was Henry behind the two headlamps, but even if he did, the kid had to be scared

212

in the damp darkness alone. Andrew was little more than a child. Likely as not, he'd take the chance of being seen by this time, hoping to get himself picked up.

He waited at the corner. The fireball preacher in the camp meeting now seemed an absurd memory, but the images of the Kick-off replayed in his mind—men and women, dressed up in their finest, the absolute epitome of lower-middle class achievement. Something of a happiness contest too, the lovely, wide smiles of sanctification worn like a badge. Always there were smiles, always laughing. Always a sweet, sweet spirit. As if a frown was demonic. And now it was all darkness, all a wet, lake mist.

He turned right again, his lights sweeping over Spurgeon Hall like a giant brush of whitewash. By the time he shifted into high, he was out of town. This time he would get the kid. The thought of the preacher and his wife, and Lillian too—the thought of their anguish was justification enough for his anger. Now it was only a matter of Andrew and Henry Witten.

He steered with both hands up near the top, leaning forward in the seat, his chest nudging the wheel. The mist hung in clumps, like gossamer, no more than six feet above the pavement, outlining the conical beams of the headlamps. It forced him to slow down in spots; the frequent curves in the road kept him shifting constantly.

Then Andrew appeared a car-length or two in front of him, running slowly, arms hanging down. He was tired. The thought of killing the boy right then and there gripped Henry Witten, and his mind offered innumerable reasons, rapid-fire. The preacher's face, beaten, reappeared. He slowed. Andrew looked back but made no move towards the woods. He simply ran on. Henry yelled at the boy, pulling the Chevy alongside.

"Andrew, forget it. Can't you see this whole thing is useless!"

But he ran on. Henry could see the wetness in his deep brown hair, mist and sweat commingled in lines around his temples, his hair in clumps.

"Andrew, for God's sake, your family loves you."

But the boy didn't respond, never looked toward the

213

car, just ran, his arms swinging low in fists.

Nothing was left to be said. There were no more arguments, no more reasons—nothing.

"Andrew," he said. "Give it up. Andrew," he said, "God will forgive you—He always forgives." Henry figured God was maybe the bottom line with the boy. Kid was brought up in a manse.

The boy turned his head. "You go to hell, Henry Witten!" he said.

The Chevy eased back, but the boy kept running. Henry stayed behind him, three, four car lengths. No one had ever told him to go to hell before, and no one had ever tried to run him down—no one had ever smashed his jaw with a fist. Anger made him groan like a dying man. He swallowed, as if trying to rid himself of some awful taste. And he laughed at the sight of the kid running, the mist, the curves, the old Chevy, the myriad excuses he had for ridding the preacher of the damned curse of an adopted son. The world, he thought, would be better off without Andrew's adolescent insolence. It could be called an accident.

He pushed the accelerator, the old Chevy's second gear lifting the car forward, pushing it like it hadn't been pushed in years. And he aimed directly at the kid—dead aim. Maybe it was fear that could do it, he told himself. Maybe it was the only thing left for him to do—try to scare the hell out of him. Maybe it was the fear of God.

The engine whined in second, but he didn't let up, the boy's body appearing more and more clearly. He could see the fine print of the shirt on the boy's back. He'd scare Andrew to death. The kid deserved it. Maybe that would do it. He had to save the wretch somehow. He'd draw a bead on that stupid, adopted kid.

Andrew stopped suddenly, then turned like stupid deer into the shafts of light cutting through the mist. Henry jerked the wheel left with both arms, but the old Chevy caught him, he was sure. He could feel the collision; he heard the thump, magnified in his ears like great thunder by the instantaneous assault of guilt—because he hadn't really meant to kill him, not really. He was insane with anger, but he hadn't meant to hit the kid.

The car spun out of control. He swung the old Chevy back and it twisted violently, its right-side tires tripping on the lip of pavement, and slowly, very slowly, it seemed, the whole steely mass flipped side over side, everything rolling, tossing, over and over, the whole world, it seemed, flipping around out of control as if he were in some trance where time slowed its march to make him feel every single emotion that had ever played through him. And the very last thing he remembered feeling was the sudden quiet when finally it stopped, wedged between the wall and the grass, upside down in the mist and the smoke and the darkness.

It was the explosion that woke him. He looked up into Andrew's square forehead. The boy was leaning over him on hands and knees.

"You okay?" Andrew said.

He tried to nod his head.

"Look at that." The boy pointed back off the road.

A pillar of fire stretched skyward from the upturned Chevy.

Henry pointed at the flames with his head. "You pulled me out?"

"Yeah," he said. "You must have got knocked out. Sure you're okay now?"

Henry nodded.

The boy sat on his legs in the grass, looking up at the fire, his face in an orange pall. Slowly the whole story returned in Henry's mind—the chase, even the preacher's despair. He saw the boy smile, maybe the first smile he had ever seen on Andrew's face.

Henry raised himself on his elbows, his head still spinning, pain spinning out through his skull from the back of his head. He rubbed his eyes with his fists. He couldn't see Andrew clearly, but through the noise of the fire he could hear the kid's strange laughing.

"What's the big joke?" he said.

Andrew was sitting with his legs flat out in front of him, his arms behind him, as if it were some outdoor concert he

was watching.

"I don't know," he said. "I was thinking that it's funny in a way—it's a funny thing, you trying so hard to get me the way you're doing, you know—and then me saving you in the end. Something funny about that." He held his head up in the light from the fire. "I could have let you go right up in smoke—you know that?" He laughed again. "You'd be in there right now, burning—"

Henry watched the flames. His body felt loose, very loose, every muscle seemed almost lost from his own control, as if his arms had suddenly grown a foot longer, as if his legs had been stretched.

"I never saved a person in my life before—not once," the boy said. Sweat ran from his face like water. "You're the first one, Henry Witten."

"I thought I hit—"

"Naaw, just clunked me on the butt. Right here—" He leaned up and grabbed himself. "You know, you could have hit me if you was trying. It's lucky for me that you swerved the way you did." The smile clung there, in the glow of the flames.

"Andrew," Henry said, "you saved my life. I owe you my life—you know that?"

Andrew puckered his lips and nodded. "That's why I'm laughing," he said. He pulled his sleeve up over his forehead. "So what's it feel like to be almost dead, Henry? What's it feel like to get yourself saved from something like that—" He pointed at the car.

The sides of his throat felt chalky, made it hard for him to swallow. "I'm grateful for what you did," Henry said.

Andrew felt at his shirt pockets. "That's all you can say is 'grateful'? I figured an educated man like you could find some much fancier way of saying it than just simple like that." He pushed himself up to his feet and stood up over Henry. "Don't have a cigarette along," he said. "You got one, Henry?"

Henry shook his head.

"I guess I better get us some help from somewheres," Andrew said. "You got some blood there on your head."

Henry saw the limp when the boy walked off into the

217

mist. He looked at his watch in the glare from the fire. It was just after four in the morning, that time of day when you don't know whether to call it early or late.

Special Music

Waiting for the boy of Vander Molen gave him opportunity to think. He still hadn't told his wife that on his forty-third birthday, sitting right here at the desk of his study, he had wondered aloud if becoming a preacher had been the right decision for him to make so many years ago that he could barely remember when and where he had made the choice. Was it someplace on the farm? Or maybe walking home from school alone? Maybe there was no real "call" at all—no vision, no sudden revelation of divine intent for his life. If there ever was any crying, he had forgotten it.

Maybe there never was any kind of "decision." Maybe the whole thing had been simply predestined, and he had fallen unwittingly into the pattern, like Peter after the arrest of Christ. Maybe it was just assumed for him all along; after all, his brothers Harold and Martin had seemed to take to the team as if they were born with the reins in their hands—but when he'd enter the barn, Diamond and Betts would shake their heads scornfully, as if his mere presence were grounds for a good horse laugh or two. Once bridled, they would raise their snoots and prance out the door with a step he translated as an obvious statement of their superiority. And his brothers would get just as moody as Pa every harvest. So he would sit around and act fidgety himself—it was expected of him. Anyway, could he really help it if he liked books?

The whole Dykstra family knew he was different. By the time he was fourteen or so, when his brothers had already convinced their father that they were of much too much value at home to waste time with school, no one, not even his father, had questioned the fact that he, Corwin, the youngest and the smartest, would surely go on, first to the school down the road, then to the academy at Hull. From there, being a preacher was as natural as the return of the purple martins to the big birdhouse Harold had built one winter when the brightest son was busy reading Latin at Hull.

And after seminary, a church in Illinois, another in a small town in Michigan, a country church in Minnesota, another in Iowa, and now here in Kansas.

Three children of his own now, the eldest just short of his own height, next month turning sixteen. His own forty-fourth year had begun, forty-three passing so quickly he rarely had time to bother thinking about himself, the preacher. He was sure, now that he thought about it, that there was something he missed somewhere, something like handwriting on a wall, or a great shining light from the heavens.

The Reverend Corwin Dykstra waited patiently. So where was the boy of Vander Molen? Already five minutes late and the supper hour coming on. Not typical of the boy either. Through years of catechism, Dykstra had shown exemplary grace with Wil, who, according to the entire community, had since birth lacked the full blessings of mental clarity. Although consistently first to take a seat in the church basement catechism room, Wil Vander Molen could hardly be called the leader of his class. Dykstra would have to ring the bell two or three times to get the others in, but Wilfred would always come in early, take the fourth seat from the right, fourth row, and then wait for the others to settle in, as he hoped, around him. Of course, it rarely happened. To his classmates, Wil Vander Molen was not a particularly becoming friend.

And Dykstra cringed when Wilfred Vander Molen would raise a hand for a question or an answer, because his comments or questions or whatever they were would always be met by a campaign of giggles from the others. Teaching catechism, already a difficult job, was made no easier by Wilfred's presence, and when the boy decided to join the church with the rest of his class, Dykstra had notified the consistory before the boy had entered for his examination, that Wilfred Vander Molen was a bit peculiar —something they all knew, of course—and that the regular questions could be suspended for ones like him. So, in front of the church like all the rest, Wilfred Vander Molen had answered "YES" publicly, in that deep, striking voice of his, his volume somewhat embarrassingly high. He started to take communion—what was it now?— already four years ago, at least.

But he never was the kind of person you would notice easily. He had spent a year in Kansas City working in his uncle's lumberyard, and Dykstra was quite sure that no one in the church had really missed him. In fact, the preacher himself hadn't noted his return until Mrs. Grevengoed came to the church study little more than three weeks ago.

"The boy sings like a bird," she had said after taking her coat and hanging it from the hook at the door, just as she always did on Tuesdays, "and he plays the piano too."

Dykstra had been more than surprised. "You've got to be kidding?" he had said.

"No."

"Who on earth could have taught him?"

"Nobody did."

"Well, where did he learn?"

"In Kansas City, I guess. In the church there."

"There's no church in Kansas City."

"Some other church, I guess. Ermina's brother's church. Baptist, I guess."

He reached for his pipe and the little silver spoon he used to clean it. He knew what was coming next.

"Reverend Dykstra, it would be so good to have him sing for the church once," she said, "And just think what it would do for the boy."

Dykstra had no reason to honor the request of Mrs. Grevengoed. Special music was only a recent innovation in the church, and he was very much aware of the problems it had lately caused among the older folk. Besides, Lois

Grevengoed was hardly the type to be trusted for advice on how to structure a worship service, what with her own marriage nearly falling apart, and her three boys rarely seen on Sundays. So he took it to the consistory; their approval would release him from full responsibility if the boy pulled something strange.

He was surprised when it passed; a few of the men frowned some when he brought it up, but none of them seemed willing to raise a real objection. Not a week later he arranged with the boy's mother to have something ready for the afternoon service the day before Dykstra's birthday. The more he had worried about it, the more he had tried to comfort himself with the assurance that whatever happened, at least Wilfred Vander Molen would receive a blessing from his own participation.

But Dykstra himself was still somewhat unsure of music and its place in the worship. He was not at all unsure of Reformed doctrine, and as near as he could tell there was nothing in the song that Wil had sung that he could distinguish as "heretical" or even "Arminian," but he knew—and the knowledge came so painfully—that the boy's style certainly violated more than a century of propriety, not to mention custom. He needed no books to tell him that.

The boy had walked up to the piano with the same step brother Harold had in approaching the team for their harvest calling.

"I will be singing 'Far and Near the Fields Are Teeming,' " he said, "and I'll be hopin' that it's as big a blessin' to you as it is to me." He sat gracefully and turned to the piano, pulling back his sleeves as if unveiling something never before left exposed.

For a moment at least, Dykstra had been somewhat relieved; after all, "Far and Near" was right there within the church hymnal—at least Wilfred wouldn't be singing some of that gospel ragtime the kids picked up from their friends down at Foursquare Gospel. Vander Molen had chosen a good church hymn. The people would be pleased.

Then he began. Immediately the preacher was stunned by an almost plaintive baritone voice capable of sweeping

upward in beautiful gestures, holding the "Loooord of Haaaarvest" for what seemed hours each time it rolled through the refrain. His fingers, long and supple, flowed almost spiritually over the keys, stopping precisely when asked to accompany the delicate movements in his voice, or transforming the instrument into a kind of drum, ramming out the rhythmical body of the music whenever he held that long "Loooord." His fingers played on every key, from the deepest bass to the highest soprano, climbing and falling in startling runs that roiled Dykstra's whole frame, creating a tangible electric spirit throughout the sanctuary, a brittle tension that seemed for him nearly unbearable. Dykstra's hands gripped the arms of the pulpit chair as he waited, his chin edging forward involuntarily, like a man impatiently expecting a delightful explosion. And each refrain built upon the last, more threatening, more fearful, because more mysteriously sweet. He held the armrests tighter, his spine pinned against the cushion.

And then it was over. The preacher exhaled very slowly as his hands loosened and his shoulders sank with reverent control.

The boy said, "Amen." And the unmistakable voice of Mrs. Grevengoed echoed the word very much aloud. Never before had such a thing been heard in the old church. The stained glass seemed to sing with the echoing cadence of what had been almost frightfully witnessed by a congregation wholly unaccustomed to such flamboyant testimony.

"You'd best talk to the boy," the consistory had said when they met the next Monday evening. Not altogether sure of what it was they were condemning, they felt assured, to a man, that what they had witnessed the afternoon before was somehow very wrong, or at least, out of place, even though some of the members, and some of their wives, too, had timidly admitted that it was "different." "Pretty soon we'll be running contests around here," one of them had said, "and we'll judge the singer on the number of Amens we can throw up from the crowd. We just can't have it. It's just not right."

Reverend Dykstra didn't need the consistory to tell him

that something had gone wrong. For more than a week now he had thought over the whole business, and it had become clear to him that Wilfred Vander Molen's performance had been somewhat indecent. Yes, *indecent* was not the wrong word. It took several days for him to realize that what he had felt after the song was concluded seemed to him to be something like guilt—as if he had witnessed something indecent, as if he had stood there stark naked himself before the whole congregation, not even a pulpit to hide his shame. And furthermore, he knew he was not alone. The congregation had been almost reluctant to raise their heads following his opening prayer, the traditional greeting going almost unnoted. He read the creed to a group whose faces seemed more ready to confess sin than faith.

Then, on Thursday, it had been Wilfred's father. He had called to ask for a time he could see the Dominie, not hinting in the least at the nature of the meeting.

"Something happened to the boy," John Vander Molen had said after sitting down, his cap in his hand. "He's not been the same since he come back from the city."

Dykstra had lit his pipe easily, drawing away in long, even breaths. "I never knew the boy could sing," he said, finally exhaling.

"Ja, we always knew he could, but you know, Dominie—a boy like him, well, sometimes it's better that he don't get in front of the people too much, you know. They can make fun of him and such."

Dykstra sat forward on his chair. "But where did he learn to play the piano like that in one year?"

"Just comes to him natural. He didn't just learn it, he always could. His ma's got the talent too, but just not so good as Wilfred."

"So you knew that before?"

"Ja, we knew, but well, it's like I was sayin', we jus' thought it was smart to hold him back from all a that, ya might say."

John Vander Molen had seemed very uncomfortable. His fingers ran across the visor of his hat, back and forth, back and forth, the hat turning slowly, smoothly, in front

225

of him. He sat straight in the chair, his knees pointing in nearly opposite directions.

"Well, I guess I don't have to tell you what some of the people thought about your boy's singing."

"No, no, Dominie. I'm really sad about the whole thing. When you asked him to sing, I thought to warn you of the result, but, well, it's just that you asked the boy's mother, ya see? Like I say, when she told him—well, he just ain't been the same since he come back from the city."

Dykstra leaned back in his chair. "What do you mean by that?"

"Don't really know if I can explain it. His ma and I just don't really understand the whole thing ourselves. He says he come to know the Lord in the city. We jus' don't know what to do with him now. No sir. We jus' never had nothin' like this happen in our family before. Do ya gotta punish the boy for sayin' that he knows the Lord?" Vander Molen straightened his legs involuntarily.

"Certainly not, John, certainly not." He remembered laughing right then. Vander Molen's dilemma seemed a bit funny for a moment. A retarded kid seeing Jesus like that. John Vander Molen had looked away as if offended at the preacher's smile. The cap stopped moving through his fingers.

"It's just that now, you see, well, this is really silly, but, well, now he wants to up and go to Michigan to study to be a preacher. Sounds crazy, doesn't it? Shoot, Dominie, you know the boy. He ain't got the brains of a good horse."

"You try to talk to him about it?"

"Ja, but it's like I said—the boy's a different kid since he come back from the city. He don't listen to authority; says he's got his own. And the Lord forgive me for sayin' it, but he's got entirely too much of Jesus!" Vander Molen crossed his legs, almost ladylike. "And ya never could reason with him."

So John Vander Molen had come to the preacher's study to ask the Dominie to talk the boy out of wasting all that time and money on something everyone around knew would call on talents the boy could never hope to have.

"Did you try to tell him that seminary work would be far too difficult for him?" Dykstra asked, laying his pipe on the desk.

Vander Molen looked down at his cap. "He says the Lord tells him himself that he's got to be up and about preachin' the Word. Says he just sees Jesus at queer times— out in the field, in the barn, in bed." The man seemed exhausted by a completely unfamiliar job he was never given tools to complete. His eyes were childish, plaintive. "He's just a changed boy since he come back from the city."

Although sad, the whole thing was absolutely crazy, of course. Dykstra knew from his own experience that the boy could not hope to get through a semester of seminary training. He couldn't even write a good English sentence— how could he ever learn Greek and Hebrew? When he told his wife that John Vander Molen had requested him to convince the boy that going to seminary was foolish, she had said nothing. "Can you imagine Professor Hooks?" he had asked. "The man would have tantrums. My word, it took Wil Vander Molen just about four years to learn 'My only comfort.' It was the only question I dared ask him in front of the consistory when he made profession of faith."

"Are you going to do it?"

"Do what?"

"Talk him out of it?" Her eyebrows furrowed.

"I've got to. Listen to reason—he'll never make it. You know that as well as I do."

"So what's going to happen?"

"What do you mean?"

"To *him?*"

"Yes, to him, you heard him sing, Corwin."

And now he waited for Wilfred Vander Molen. Maybe the boy was out picking corn with the rest of the Vander Molen family. Come to think of it, it was rather stupid of him to schedule a meeting just before supper. Hadn't been that long since he walked the rows himself. The whole family had worked long hours for more than a month this time of year. John Vander Molen was probably saying to his wife right now, how that it was just like a preacher to forget that all the help was needed during harvest, and how he could have easily found some other time much more convenient to talk to the boy. Dykstra reprimanded himself for not giving the whole business enough thought. This was harvest time.

Foolish of him to forget that, but the mistake had been made anyway. So what about this boy—it's all just a matter of spelling out the truth, he told himself. No reason to get upset about such a thing; nothing's going to be hurt by it, that's sure. But hadn't John Vander Molen said the boy couldn't listen to reason? Dykstra relit his pipe and exhaled, killing the match with a funnel of smoke. It's times like these that try men's souls, he told himself. "You heard him sing," his wife had said with the voice of a mother somehow tested by an uncompromising child. The blackened matchstick turned in his fingers, its heat already gone. So how do you explain that there's got to be a limit to "knowing Jesus"—and as if that's not enough of a problem, how do you begin to explain that fact to a moronic kid who says he's seeing visions in the hayloft? Almost reluctantly, he dropped the match in the basket at the side of the desk.

When the boy finally showed, no more than twenty minutes late, Dykstra smiled to see him, like his father, dressed up in his Sunday suit to visit the preacher's study. He pulled off the gray stocking cap, and his brown hair, knotted and matted, looked like a broken bale of year-old straw. He stood at the door and waited to be formally admitted, his slow-moving eyes wandering over the books that stood around and behind the preacher's broad, rectangular desk.

"Come in, Wilfred," Dykstra said, rising and pointing at a convenient chair. "Will you please sit down?"

The boy moved cautiously, keeping a polite eye on the preacher as his hands moved behind him to plot the way to the straight-back chair in front of the desk. "Sure is alotta books you got, Reverend Dykstra. Did ya read 'em all?"

"No, Wilfred, not all. Preachers get many books—some you use occasionally; others just wait, I guess."

Wilfred kept his cap out in front of him to keep his hands busy. Dykstra turned to the shelves himself, as if to indulge the boy's emotion.

"My pa is got some books too, but some of 'em—most all of 'em, I think, is in the Dutch language. What he got from his pa before him. Can't understand 'em anyway. He don't read 'em no more. They just sit there up on the cupboard with the Bible."

"Well, if you ever want to borrow any of these, Wil, just ask and I'll help you find something good."

"No kiddin'? Never was one for readin', though. Always like farm work. Pa like me to work by him on the farm."

"Didn't you ever get a chance to go to school?"

"Sure. Went over three years down to Mapledale. Besides, I been all those years in catechism." He sat forward in the chair. "Really enjoyed that. Ma used to read it all to me the night before. Pa said it was right for me to have some church knowledge—'Everybody's got to have some knowledge of church things, no matter how dumb'—that's what he used to say." He laughed.

Dykstra smiled politely. "Well, just the same, if your mother ever consents to read some to you and you want to borrow any, you just don't be afraid to ask."

"Well, maybe I'll take one of 'em along today. Ya got any on Jesus?"

The pipe was cold in his hands. He searched for a match, smiling. "I guess you might say that they're all on Jesus in some way."

"All-um?"

"I guess so." Dykstra noted the boy's eyes again. They were dull—gray and slow. You could always see it in the eyes, he told himself. It was a dead giveaway.

"Wouldn't ever guess that all them books could be written on just Jesus. Is all of 'em true?"

"Well, I guess so. I guess it depends on what you believe—"

Wilfred raised his cap on his hand as if it were a veiled man. "Well, I believe in Jesus, Reverend. He saved me when I was in the city."

"I guess I didn't mean it quite that way, boy. Some of them are about the historical Jesus—who he was, how he lived—you know, things like the Pharisees and such. Some are about the parables; some about miracles. Jesus Christ was a fascinating man."

"Jesus saved me when I was working in the lumberyard in Kansas City, sir. I know that Jesus is my Savior."

Dykstra poked at the ashes in the pipe. "Maybe we ought to talk about that a while, Wilfred." He put the pipe in his mouth, unlit, and leaned back in the desk chair, rocking slightly. "I'm very interested in knowing a little more about how exactly that happened. Jesus is very close to me, you know, being the preacher and all here in town." The boy spun his gray stocking cap in his fingers, almost like his father had done. His hands were still hidden beneath; his feet were locked up beneath the chair. "You think you can kind of explain to me exactly what it was that happened to you?" He sat up forward in his chair, his pipe in his mouth, his eyes narrowed like a curious child's.

Vander Molen sat back and raised one leg over the other. "Ain't nothin' to splain at all."

The preacher frowned.

"He just up and saved me—just like that." Momentarily, one of his hands appeared, two fingers snapped, and the hand retreated beneath the cap.

"From what?"

"Whatcha mean, 'from what'?"

"Well, from falling lumber or a big table saw or something like that?"

"What?"

"*From*, Wilfred—what did he save you from?"

"From sin."

"From sin?"

"Ja."

"Nothing else?"

"Naw, never had no trouble there in the yard. Pa always said I was born to work with wood. Uncle Jake says I'm the best yardman he ever had down there in the city."

Dykstra put both elbows on the table. "Well, how did he save you then?"

"Just a miracle is all—he jus' saved me from all my sin!"

"But how did he come to you, Wil?" Dykstra brought a fist down hard on the desk. "How can you be sure that you saw him?" He looked down and saw for the first time that a ring of manure, brown like horseradish mustard, haloed Wilfred's boots. "How did he come to you and tell you that you were saved?" Did you really hear him speak to you? I want to know." He extended both arms toward the boy.

Vander Molen's eyes dropped quickly, then wandered back up and along the shelves around the desk. "Can't really say. I ain't one to be writin' no books, you know." His eyes dropped back to the cap he held in his hands.

Once more Dykstra searched through his top drawer for a match, scattering pencils and rubberbands with his hands. "Well, you might not be a writer, but you sure can sing." The comment was offhanded, almost sarcastic, and obviously misinterpreted.

"An' did ya like my song on Sunday?" The comment had reawakened a smile. Vander Molen raised his head.

Those dull gray eyes, remarkably lucid, almost aglow with anticipation, faced him straight on, and Dykstra knew suddenly what his wife had meant. The music. "Speak to the boy," the consistory had said. He raised his right hand to his forehead and flipped through the pages of a commentary with the fingers of his left hand. He looked back up, his right hand acting as a kind of visor, as if he were shielding his eyes from a blinding heat.

"Well, let me just say that I was amazed—we all were—at your talent." Dykstra watched the boy closely. If there was any sign of reaction, it was a rather indefinite weakening of his smile. He pushed further. "What I mean to say is that everyone in church was really surprised at what a musician you really are!"

Vander Molen's eyes fell to the cap. He coughed slightly to clear his throat, and instinctively a hand emerged to cover his mouth.

"I mean no one really knew you could even sing, much less play the piano."

"Ma and pa knew. So did Jesus."

"Well, I, for one, am really happy that I know, because now I know where we can go for more special music when we need it in the church."

Wilfred sat up straight in the chair. "Then I can sing agin

sometimes? Pa was sure you'd tell me that I couldn't never sing anymore in the church."

Dykstra laughed. "No, I think it can be arranged alright, but we'll have to change some things—"

"Oh, Reverend Dykstra, I'll practice hard—no more mistakes."

"It wasn't mistakes I was thinking about, Wilfred. You see, we belong to a special group, a group called 'Reformed,' and I think you ought to know that what we do and what we sing, what we preach and what we confess, may not be exactly the same business as that church where you found Jesus in Kansas City."

"First Church of the Ice Box."

"What's that?"

"I said, 'First Church of the Ice Box.' "

"Strange name for a church."

"You got it wrong, Reverend. 'First Church of the Ice Box' is what Pastor Tom used to say about lotsa churches. And I know what he meant too. This here church what we belong to is the First Church of the Ice Box."

Dykstra sat up quickly and stared across the desk at the boy.

"I know what yer sayin' because Pa says to me the same things. He says, 'Jus' don't talk so much about Jesus.' He says it makes Jesus cheap to be sayin' 'Praise the Lord for the sunshine,' an' 'Praise the Lord for the mashed potatoes.' And he says, 'Don't be singin' that way—ya gotta learn to control yerself some, boy.' "

Dykstra banged his pipe bowl into the square glass ashtray on the desk.

"Well, someday I'm gonna be a reverend, Reverend, and when I am, bells will be ringin' in my soul. And I'm gonna be preachin' the whole gospel—nothin' but Jesus saves. And in my church we're gonna have happiness and joy and lotsa music and testimony."

The cap dropped from his hands, and he leaned forward at the waist, staring at the preacher, his gray eyes tinged with silver and red like the last glowing log of an abandoned campfire. Dykstra's fingers searched his pockets for the last match, but found nothing. He grabbed at his lapels, and his fingers found the buttons, closing them as if he could shield his chest from the cold of an unseen draft. He rolled his chair backward to the shelves, and snapped out an old Greek text from his seminary days.

"Come here, boy," he said. "Now look at this."

Vander Molen stood, then walked around the desk and stopped at the preacher's side. Dykstra paged through the book, stopping at random. He slapped the book on the surface of the desk and looked up toward the door, speaking to an image in the chair. "Read this," he said.

Wilfred looked over the preacher's shoulder at the text. He bent over awkwardly. Dykstra could feel his breathing. "Here, look at it yourself," he said, handing the boy the book, then pushing his chair away from the desk and the boy.

Wilfred stared at the text, almost as though he were studying. He drew the book up close to his gray eyes. Dykstra watched him. The boy's eyebrows arched low over his eyes and his head jerked, slightly to the left, then right, and back again, as if he were reading. "Guess maybe I need glasses," he said. "These words don't look like nothin' I ever seen before." His concentration centered on the page. He held the book further away, trying to focus his eyes. "Bet my Ma could read it to me."

Dykstra braced himself by holding to the chair. "Wil, your mother couldn't read it either, nor your father, nor your brothers. But if you plan on bein' a preacher, you have to be able to read things like this." He grabbed the text from the boy. "Listen to me now; see if you recognize this—'The Lord is my shepherd, I shall not want—.'"

"Course. That's from the Bible. I'd sure recognize that anywhere."

Dykstra slammed the book to the desk and turned to face the boy, trying to gather his emotion into one more assault. "Now listen to me, Wil, 'cause I'm going to tell you the truth. You couldn't make it as a preacher, you hear me? If you can't read the Bible, you can't pass the seminary. To be a preacher you've got to be educated. Some can do it, some can't." He looked up. The boy's face, still brightened, held its challenge.

"But Pastor Tom says that with God all things is possible."

" 'All things' may be going a little too far. The pastor's right to a point, however." Dykstra retrieved his pipe and held it between his thumb and forefinger, using it as a pointer. "You got any stallions, Wil?"

"Course."

"Any of them going to be having colts this spring?"

The boy let out an instinctive chuckle. "That's crazy—no stallion's gonna be havin' colts on our farm or anybody else's farm that I ever known of."

"Well, let me tell you something Wilfred. There's some boys that will never be preachers—just like there's some horses that will never have colts. Some boys will be farmers, some will be teachers, some will work in the lumberyards, and some will be preachers. You see what I'm trying to tell you, boy? You'll never be a preacher—you can't even read the Bible."

Vander Molen stepped back, picked the cap off the floor, and covered his hands once again. His eyes moved quickly downward, over the desk, the rug, his shoes, then up over his Sunday suit. He pulled the cap down over his ears, and put both hands out in front of him on the desk leaning over the preacher.

Dykstra reminded himself that he could see it in the boy's eyes.

Wilfred breathed heavily, but the words wouldn't come.

Dykstra stood. "But you can be a preacher in whatever you do, Wil. Even if you work with wood in the yard in the city, or with your Pa on the farm. You ought to know that. The Lord loves all of us equally. Go back to your uncle's yard—let that be your calling. Be a preacher there. Take some comfort from that, boy."

Wilfred Vander Molen leaned back and stood erect, as if the words had finally been granted him. " 'My only comfort in life and death—' " he stopped, deliberately—"I almost forgot."

And Dykstra knew why he left just then, because he saw the weakness forming in his lips. He knew the tears would run cold in the damp fall air outside the church.

When the door closed behind him, the preacher dropped the unlit pipe into the ashtray, brought both elbows up on the desk, and held his head in his hands. The Greek text lay beneath him. It was Plato's *Republic*.

Dykstra, unwilling to face his wife, found himself looking forward to the harvest.

Factory Second

George Wieskamp, leaning up against the side of the church, ran his pointer finger down the sharp crease in his collar and tugged it lightly, as if it were chafing his neck. He listened to Hank Wanders out of a sense of obligation to the men around him.

"So I'z on de north end, up here, right?" Wanders' thick middle finger jabbed into the grass. "An' most de guys is drivin' up from de south, down here." With his left hand he swept through the grass like a giant comb. "Hadn't seen anybody else for hours. Thought sure we wuz the only guys in de whole area."

Wieskamp had heard the story before, too often. He pushed back his shoulder blades and rubbed his back against the brick like a cat.

"So anyways I'm just here waitin', right? Thinkin' dat something oughtta get scared up by de drive. I'm watchin' too, course; you know I got me an eight-pointer postin' like dat right here on de lakeshore." He sniffed hard and drew his huge hand from wrist to fingertip beneath his nose. Wieskamp winced, turning his head away. "So I knew what I wuz doin'." He looked up nodding, hoping for approval. "I knew what to watch for and how to listen."

The men of the church sat and stood around like a gallery, their boys obviously entranced by Hank Wanders. Wieskamp watched his own boy sitting quietly, his knees beneath him, eyes wide in anticipation.

"Well then, outa nowhere des shots come—phhht,

phhht, phhht—you know, the way you can just hear 'em in de air, and couldn't a been too high neither. Just up here." One of his huge arms measured a distance the size of a top hat above his bald head.

"I didn't move a damn inch."

Wieskamp glanced up quickly, looking for the women, who stood, like the men, circled into a group like an old wagon train, nodding and talking far out of the range of Wanders' thick voice.

"You mean you stayed standin' up, Hank?"

"Oh, no, I know when to get my butt down, son. Soon as I caught de whistle, I wuz like this—" he raised both arms above his head, "—flat on the ground, kissin' mother earth."

"Anyway, didn't hear no more for awhile, musta been ten minutes or so. So I reared back and raised my head—had an orange cap on too, mind you—just raised it up a bit, like this," he leaned back, "till I could see what's goin' on. Right over my head. Heard one smack into a pine. Made a thud, kinda—thwaaat—like that."

Wieskamp couldn't take any more, but he waited it out, fully aware of the end of the attack.

Wanders raised both of his arms as if he were carrying his Winchester. He looked around, gun in hand.

"Now I'm talkin' about my life, you understand. I wan't about to take another round between the eyes, see, so I brought up that gun slowly and emptied the clip in de direction of where I thought them shots come from. I just let 'em go, crackin' close as thunder." He stopped, and no one spoke.

"Never heard another noise, no sir. Never checked it out either." He stood back for a moment, arms across his chest, his biceps flattened into bulging thighs. Thin, gray-black hair grew like a fine mist across his back and shoulders and darkened into fur across a chest the size of a TV wrestler's.

No one laughed. George Wieskamp rubbed his clean-shaven chin and checked the food line starting to form near the parking lot. The lake breeze had cooled off the hot July afternoon, and the air was sharp with the smell of the fry—

burning charcoal and hot grease from hamburgers and brats.

"Jeeez!" One of the kids was still mesmerized. Wieskamp watched them slowly unwind from the tension, settling back on their hands or picking long blades of grass to shove between their teeth. Wieskamp laughed angrily. And him coming to the annual Sunday School picnic dressed that way—nothing over him but an undershirt, not even a T-shirt, mind you, but an old-fashioned brief with two thin straps running like ruts through all that darn hair on his shoulders.

"Looks to me like the brats are done," somebody said, and like sheep the men moved over toward the lot, picking up their wives and daughters on the way.

Dorothy Wieskamp held out a plate and cup to her husband while she reached in a grocery bag for a fork and a spoon. "Henry again?" She didn't bother looking up for an answer.

"And the same old story too. Heard it at least three times before. You'd think everyone would know it already." Her husband flicked a ladybug off her sleeve and reached for his utensils, tightly wrapped in a flowered napkin the same pattern as the paper plate.

George left his wife at the end of the serving line, his plate filled with cole slaw, baked beans, and a couple of double brats. He wandered back to the men who had reconstructed their little circle, and sat reluctantly on the grass, worried he might stain his new off-white double-knits.

"Bout time for Crazy Days, George?" Hank Wanders looked up from his sandwich.

"Just a couple of weeks yet." George spooned up some baked beans, wiping his lips with his napkin.

"Got some good sales comin'?"

"Always do, don't I?"

"You can bet this guy'll be first in line again," Wanders said, pointing a thumb at his heart. "That Crazy Days is one fine tradition." He wiped his chin with his forefinger, then sucked off the spilled ketchup as if it were frosting.

"Me and the wife wuz down to Collinsville, what, a

week ago or so. Gotta new store down there—factory outlet, I guess they call it. Nothin' there but seconds. Cheap place. Darn cheap."

Wieskamp bit lightly on his double brat, his face turned toward the stand.

"Anyway, got some things there. Bought this sweater-like shirt, you know." He picked at his undershirt as if to explain the fabric. "Thought I got myself a real bargain—wuz just $2.99 plus tax. Darn good shirt for three bucks, I figured. Told the wife I couldn't afford to pass it up." He forked in some cole slaw. "Got the thing home and showed it to my girls. Good lookin' shirt, I thought. Kinda' brown up here," he rubbed his shoulder, "then orange—not orange like an orange, more like a pum'kin—down around the belly."

George Wieskamp stopped eating and watched the fire behind the food stand. Bad enough having to listen to the jackass, but now he's taking away all my customers, sending them all off to Collinsville for some trash clothes. Hope the seams split.

"Good lookin' shirt, yessir. Couldn't find a thing wrong with it—you gotta kinda check dem things over down there, you know. But it hadda be a second, sure, otherwise they wouldn't be sellin' it in de store down there, right? Well, that's what I'm thinkin'. So anyway, my daughter says to put it on and show it off and all, so I pulled it over my shirt here and she takes one look at it on me and she busts out laughin' so hard she can barely talk."

He threw in the last of his beans and said nothing.

"Well, what was it Hank?"

"The darn thing was backwards!"

"Backwards?"

"Ja, backwards. You know—it was sewn kaflooie—inside out. The buttons was all sewed on the inside, or what was supposed to be de inside of de dumb thing. Jees, I felt like an idiot, 'specially since ya can't bring nothin' back to dat place."

George Wieskamp took a big bite out of his bratwurst.

The Sunday School picnic was just another in a long list

of provocations that Wieskamp felt were personal affronts to him as a fellow member of the congregation. If seventy times seven was the minimum requirement, then surely he had already suffered upwards of four hundred, especially if he counted all the stories he had only heard about the brute.

After Thursday night's picnic Wieskamp had spent a half hour trying to explain to his own son that the stupid story about the deer hunting trip had no, absolutely no really important lessons for a young Christian boy. After all, there was nothing so darn loving about unloading a clip at an unseen target with the stated purpose of ending what certainly was a mistake to begin with, was there? Where was the concern for another man's welfare in that act? Where the forgiveness? His son sat quietly in front of him on the front porch, looking down at the golf ball in his hands, cleaning out the specks of dirt from the indentations with his fingernail.

And the kid had the unmitigated gall to ask, not two days later, mind you, if he could go out to Henry Wanders' place, 'cause Mr. Wanders (can you believe that—Mr. Wanders) had told him he'd love to help him learn to shoot the bow that his own father had given the boy for his birthday in May. Just incredible! Everything he had said went right out the other ear; the vile story stayed, of course. So what could he say? No, you can't associate with that trash? Of course not. The kid would never understand how he meant that.

And after all, archery (and why didn't he think of that when he bought the kid a present) was the cause of half of Hank Wanders' problems. So what if he was the best shot in Sheboygan County? Who really cared? The kid didn't know that it was that fancy bow of his that kept Hank Wanders flying around the whole state of Wisconsin most every weekend between April and September, including Sundays, of course, since most all the big meets were on Sundays, the day when he oughta have been lunked in church with those thieving little kids and his robust wife. They never came without him. So nobody came during the summers, just about all summer long. So what was it—three years ago already when Wieskamp himself was chosen as the representative of the church council, named to officially express their feelings concerning Wanders' church attendance, or lack of it, during the summer months. My goodness, if the kid were only old enough to understand all of that business. But he wasn't yet, so what's a man to say to his boy in that kind of position?

That was all last week already, but now he had taken enough. He was going there again, representing only himself and his family this time, bound and determined to make a significant impact on the hard-headed louse, no matter what Wanders would try to say. His wife had told him the story after work, how one of the Wanders' kids, a boy, the second oldest (they must have least a dozen), had ridden that brand new Wards ten-speed down the street (and where did they get the money for that if they couldn't afford the church budget). How one of the neighbor's kids must have whipped something harmless at just the wrong time, and how the Wanders' kid (and is it any wonder with the kind of bringing up they've had) swerved out of the way, nearly heading into the path of an upcoming car, then turning back and letting out a string of cuss words that Dorothy herself wouldn't repeat, they were so vile. Right there in town—in front of all the neighbor's houses. Right there with the Wieskamp's youngest, Julie, just past three, standing open-mouthed, amazed at the Wanders' kid because he was so angry. He wanted to know what those words were, because he wanted to write them down and bring them personally to Hank Wanders on a silver platter, so to speak, but Dorothy couldn't get up enough nerve to tell him exactly what had been said. "Spell 'em out here," he had said, shoving her a notepad marked "Wieskamp's Clothing for Men and Boys." "Just don't care to," she had said. "C'mon, how can I confront the old man?" But she wouldn't. She told him to just think once of the worst ones he remembered from the army. "Yer kidding!" he said. "Yep." He felt a sharp pain through his brain. So he wrote some down himself before he left.

And on top of everything else, it was Wanders who was

divorced, the only man in the Easton Dutch Church, a fact which accounted for a number of additional headaches—if he were keeping track, at least 150 of the total. Time after time the consistory had been out there burning the midnight oil. He heard all about it in the back room of the store, and he complained to some of the others about the church shirking its responsibilities by not throwing the bum out. Let him go to the Presbyterians, for Pete's sake, like all the rest who couldn't take the heat. But no. There were some gutless ones who seemed to refuse to act decisively, and all the while Wanders would smile and joke with the others, making outright mockery of church discipline. And the guy even took communion. Everytime it was served, he'd be sure to show up, as if he could catch the smell of wine on a stiff west wind. And it was celebrated only four times per year.

But this was too far. George Wieskamp had put up with divorce, church-skipping, the public school, those barbaric T-shirts his kids wore around town, his wife's breast feeding in the middle of the church, bawling babies, and Sunday archery tournaments (including full, standing portraits in Monday's Press captioned, "Easton's Wanders Captures Richland Center Tourney," pictures that told the world about Wanders' brazen defiance of everything the Dutch church stood for). So he drove like a maniac down the road to the lake, ready to hand out some good old hellfire and brimstone. After all, the way he lives his own life is one thing, but when his kids threaten to corrupt the others in the village, someone has got to act.

And so what if Hank Wanders had huge biceps and a chest wide as an axe-handle. Wieskamp certainly didn't intend to fight, only to preach, to tell the animal that if he allowed his kids to use those army words at home, that was one thing—but if they went around yelling them in the ears of three-year-old girls, then they were bound for big trouble, not only with George Wieskamp, but also with a number of other concerned parents. And although Wieskamp understood that his emotion was just a hair out of hand, he felt confident that he was embarked on a holy crusade, fraught with divine inspiration.

He crossed the interstate and entered the lakeshore area, reminding himself as he passed the 7-11 of how someone had told him about seeing Henry's overweight, second wife spend twenty-five big ones (plus food stamps!) for groceries in a convenience store where even a small jar of creamy Skippy was at least a nickel more than at Lemke's Red Owl in Easton. There was no excuse for such squandering.

The Wanders' homestead was indeed unique—perhaps *peculiar* would be a better word, he thought. For while Henry had never built a conventional home he had (who knows why) assembled a variety of dwellings—a one-room log cabin blackened with pitch on the outside, a basement house with nothing but a periscope-like door above the ground, and a medium-to-large size house trailer where his family based their operations. It was an embarrassment for already unnerved consistory members. They had to check all three sometimes before finding the family for *huis bezoek*. He drove in the driveway past a pile of two by twelves surrounded by prairie grass and parked up next to the old storm door entrance to the basement house. It must be the coolest place during the summer heat.

Wanders kept no lawn. Weeds grew in thick clumps everywhere on the four or five acre plot others may have called a yard, creeping jenny long ago strangling any possibility for what Wieskamp would have called respectable landscaping. Fortunately, he thought, a half dozen pines bordered the driveway, blocking a view of the place which he figured Ladybird herself would have otherwise condemned as unAmerican. For the only thing that Wanders seemed to prefer to guns and bows was plain old junk, as much as he could store and more. Old stoves and refrigerators stood like white ghosts in the weeds, single file, as if coming directly off an assembly line—and not a one of them in working condition either, you can bet. Behind a rusted swing-set was a chicken-wire pen, long ago victim of wind and winter, but before that home to hundreds of young ringneck pheasants, part of a typical Wanders business scheme designed to capitalize on all the dumb Milwaukee hunters heading north up the interstate as if northern Wisconsin were southwest Africa. Its sides bulged now, at least where the fence still stood. Wieskamp just shook his head. Another old project, likewise abandoned, was eternally memorialized by two long rows of aluminum roofing where in the not too distant past Wanders had operated a mink farm. The cages were gone now, sold at a discount to some other unlikely sucker surely, but piles of droppings rose beneath the roofs like little mountains, their sculptured peaks edging above the weeds. Between the mink farm and the log cabin was enough cord wood to last the family through four lakeshore winters, and behind the cabin, far to the north of the lot, three coon hounds, brown and gray, swayed back and forth in their cage as if performing some obligatory religious ceremony, baying occasionally in a mournful contralto, less fearsome than irritating. Wieskamp could do little more than laugh at the whole business.

Aside from the hounds there was little sound on the Wanders' place, and George Wieskamp felt sure when he rapped on the storm door that there would be no reply. Not that there were no cars around. Out behind the coon hounds Wieskamp saw at least four old Studebakers, and right in front of the trailer a '57 Ford wagon afflicted with terminal cancer. A twelve-foot flatbed truck was parked up by the firewood, and a three-wheel Cushman scooter, still Post Office blue, leaned up against one of the old stoves. So who could have guessed what they were driving? Whatever it was, he told himself, it probably wasn't there. After all, several of the Wanders' delinquents would be out in the junk yard if they were home; they had so darn many kids—"yours, mine, and ours," Wanders would say with a smile—since that big woman, his second wife, had also been married before. All they needed now was some adopted Orientals, Wieskamp thought—and why not? The place was a zoo already.

He backed away from the door and stepped on a rusty can of Mountain Dew, nearly losing his balance, letting slip an expletive his wife would never have allowed. He could see from the distance that the cabin was padlocked, so he turned to the trailer and walked over the gravel to the other side of the road, kicking bottle caps as if he were a child. He had not forgotten his original mission, of course; the thought of such words in his own daughter's ear rekindled the anger quickly, but he was quite sure now that no one was at home. With nothing but quiet all around him, he approached the trailer, suddenly feeling himself on a wholly different mission—an intelligence mission, secretly spying on this alien Wanders clan, poking and prying, analyzing garbage like some reporters he had read about in *Newsweek*, looking for some secret to a clear and explainable understanding of evil itself—how to illustrate all of this to his only son, something to make the kid understand the unique blessing of his own heritage. The pines blocked the view from the road, and even if someone did see him he could always say he was here representing the church, which was, certainly, quite true in its own way.

He knocked on the aluminum door of the trailer, obligated to go through the formalities, already eyeing the spaces between the trailer and hounds where piles of hardware seemed to be lying around as if on display in a 24-hour flea market. No one answered. He walked around the back like some kind of TV detective looking for the ultimate clue, aimed directly north toward the bull's eye targets pinned on perpendicular bales of straw. That was when he smelled it. Smoke. He looked first toward the cabin but saw nothing, then the woodpiles, the basement house, and even across the field of standing corn at a neighboring farm. Nothing. It was too strong. It was coming from the trailer. He put his hand on the side and felt it hot. He turned back around the corner and saw smoke sneaking almost mystically from a combination window, its glass still down from the winter. There must be a fire. He put both hands against the metal, as if doubting what he had felt. There was no doubt. The trailer was on fire.

He ran back to the front step, his mind racing with alternatives. He opened the aluminum door, grabbed the knob of the wooden storm door and pushed. Locked. Jackass locks his doors, as if he's got something others might want! He backed up, still for barely a second. There were no telephone lines to the basement house, none to the black cabin. Must be in the trailer. He ran for the door lowering his head as he jumped up the steel steps, then slamming up against the storm with his shoulder. It didn't budge. He saw smoke seeping from a closed window and rising from the breather pipe. The steps in front made an ordinary assault impossible. He turned and ran back to the basement house where he had seen a wrecking pole in the grass. He found it quickly and flew back, holding the six foot pipe like a pole vaulter. Never breaking stride, he rammed it into the wood just beneath the knob and the door popped open like a bottle, taking some of the door mount with it in fractured pieces. Smoke was visible through the open door; it hung like a cloud at the ceiling. Again he thought of calling, but he could spend precious time just hunting for the phone. He grabbed a handkerchief from his back pocket and held it over his mouth and nose.

Water. The kitchen was to the right of the entrance. Cupboards banged open. No pots even. A few glasses. He could hear flames snapping in the back. Then it hit him. Some of the family could be still in here. He rushed through a living room area and into the thick smoke, yelling like a child, his voice cracking into falsetto in the searing heat. He heard no reply. The first bedroom area was empty except for a trophy case. The second was on fire. Flames climbed the curtains in yellow horror. He kept the cloth to his mouth; his eyes stung so much he wished he could sit and cry. But there was no one there. He turned back toward the entrance, grabbed four books off the shelf in the front and threw them through the windows, sure that smoke would find quicker exit there, but the fire responded to the additional air by moving closer, like a flower opening to the sun. He ran back through the hall and jumped out the doorway. For a second he held his hands to his eyes, trying to think of what to do. He knew he couldn't possibly put it out. There was no chance of running a half-mile down the road to the Roerdinks to call the Easton Fire Department; the trailer would be long gone by the time they arrived. That left salvage as the only alternative. Quickly he assessed what he had seen inside, his hands still rubbing his eyes. He spit on the cloth and rubbed it into his lids, as if he could wash out the sting. A trophy case. Some books, a television, a long console hi-fi. Some clothes. Pictures. Furniture.

He ran back in, trying to tie the handkerchief around his face like some bank thief. He started in the living room. First the TV. He jerked out the cord and antenna as he carried it out and down the steps, dropping it maybe fifteen feet away from the trailer. An armchair. He literally threw it from the front step. A leg cracked when it hit the ground. Another chair, a rocker. A library case, books spilling from his grasp like water from a bucket. Whenever he could he shut his eyes, trying to make them tear. The fire grew louder. He let the couch sit. The console hi-fi was old. He hesitated for what he knew was too many valuable seconds. Thing wasn't worth $35. He picked it up, back muscles straining, and dropped it outside, the bandanna dropping from his face.

Now what? The trophies. He knew the case was closer to the fire, and he knew at the same moment what Wanders would treasure. He wrapped the handkerchief around himself again and headed back in, knowing it would be the last trip. The living room was thick with smoke, but it was almost cleaned. He shut his eyes and pushed through it, his mind racing through second guesses. Let the damn things go. Teach the sucker a lesson. Let 'em melt into nothing. Let Wanders see his god melted and charred like so much soot. Who cares? Who could blame him? He was already a hero. Who would ever know? Small flames crept out of the back bedroom and into the bathroom that separated Wanders' trophy room from the back of the trailer. The heat was growing intense. Rugs burned on the floor, walls lit up like wooden matchsticks. The trophy case was huge. Its veneer was peeling away from the side closest to the heat. Take them, he told himself. The stupid things are probably not replaceable. He kicked the glass out with his shoe and grabbed several in his arms. Then he turned and flung them out of the window, returned and grabbed more, little Robin Hoods with drawn bows poking into his ribs. The trailer was rapidly going. He scooped up what he could and left, his throat sharp and dry in the dense smoke. When he left the trailer for the last time, he leaned over like a man temporarily sick to his stomach, the trophies falling from his arms as his muscles finally relented to the smoke's strangulation. He coughed from deep in his lungs, his breath coming hard, forcing more coughing, until he dropped in the weeds, his lungs erupting.

The Roerdinks helped him to his feet, and by the time the Easton emergency squad had clamped the oxygen mask over his face, he had almost recovered. His stomach felt brittle and his eyes stung, open or shut. He watched the red lights flash over the pines and heard the tanker spit out water at the remains. The metal walls had melted like solder, only the steel joists standing on the blackened frame, running up and down the sides like the bars of an old prison.

"Total loss," he heard someone say, as if there was even something worth losing in the darn fire—as if anything of real value could have gone up. He sat up on the car seat, watching the jets of water douse what remained of the embers. The chairs and things he had saved were hauled clear from the heat and were being used by sightseers watching what remained of a long lost battle.

There was never any mistaking Hank Wanders. Vision half obscured, Wieskamp saw the man coming at more than one hundred yards, the white undershirt lit up against his chest. He hadn't forgotten the reason for his coming, but a sense of discretion kept him from bringing it up now.

Wanders' face was blackened, sweat dripping from his chin and coating his throat in a greasy sheen. "Wieskamp," he said, reaching out his hand, "I'm indebted." He coughed into his left hand. "There wasn't a damn thing in there, really, but I'm grateful for the trophies."

When Wieskamp laughed, his lungs tightened and he resumed coughing.

"I think yer partly a fool, though. Nothin' in that darn trailer was worth bettin' yer life. Nothin' at all. But I'm grateful anyways, ya hear?"

Wieskamp drew his lips into a wiry smile. Wanders'

hand was hot and wet.

A month later in August, the cool lake breeze never came and the night stayed hot and muggy. He awoke coughing from the recurring dream of flames and smoke and himself, George Wieskamp, bound by some sub-conscious force, watching his own home being gutted, as if he couldn't decide what should be saved from his own total loss.

Poodles Corner

She felt like a character in an old Saturday night movie, outside the rush of snow floodlit by the dead Mustang's headlights. It was altogether too much like a story, and she hated to douse the lights because she knew that the swirling world would disappear into a dark flash. She jammed the last of her cigarette into the ash tray. She was alone now. The radio was off.

It was too much like a story except it was happening, not three miles from her stepfather's place. She would have made it through the storm if it weren't for the fact that the Mustang had run out of gas. "Take the Buick," her stepfather had said when he warned her about the storm, but she never felt at ease in his big black car, that huge thing, like some kind of limo.

She knew exactly where she was. Her car pointed straight east into town, off the shoulder of county trunk AA, not more than a couple of city blocks past the old DX station on Poodles Corner. It was her luck there too; only she would run out of gas this close to a station that hadn't sold a pint of gas in a decade, in the worst storm of the winter—February and deathly cold—and nobody else in Easton stupid enough to be out of their dens on such a night. All because she had run out of gas. She never thought of gas when she was in the city, never thought of it at all. She turned off the ignition, and her own little interior world of amber dash lights darkened.

Outside, the volleying wind cut the silence, and shafts of cold bore in like some unyielding commitment. She could just wait here forever, she told herself. Freezing to death might not be a bad way to go, just nodding off into the ease of sleep. Made her smile to think of it—going that way. And tomorrow, the storm long gone some place east over the lake, someone—maybe Jiggs Dekker from the old DX—someone would find her right here, the Mustang clogged up with white. He'd scrape off the snow from the windows with his arm or a broom—light snow, snow like powder in the frigid wake of the blizzard. And he would find her there in the front seat, slumped over the wheel. She wondered if frozen people turned blue.

And someone would call her stepfather. They would find him at the office, and he'd be worried sick, up all night probably, waiting for her to call him from the city. But he wouldn't know what to say when they'd tell him about her death. He'd be paralyzed with grief—the same way he was when she told him about Rosendale, her decision to go with the others, to leave for the camp out West. Though he had said nothing at first, she saw the fear in his eyes—for her safety, she supposed. So unreasonably concerned for a man who was only her stepfather anyway. As if she didn't have to live her own life sometime, as if she didn't have to be someone herself someday.

"It's the wrong choice," he told her finally.

"How do you know?" she had said. "You've never been out of Easton in your whole life."

"I'm sure it's the wrong choice," he had said again, both hands on his desk, as if he could raise it with his will.

"Jesus tells me it's the right decision, and I'm going," she had told him, trying to hide her shaking from his eyes. And there they stood, both of them, staring at each other, their hands down.

"So it's Jesus, is it?" He had looked up at the ceiling then, stood back and gazed up as if there were some kind of portrait image up there. "Jesus isn't sending me the same message," he said at last. "I don't know that it's Jesus telling you anything. It's that cult!"

"There's nothing you can say," she said. "I'm going."

Maybe that was her greatest moment, telling him she was going and then doing it too. A cult, he called it, but cult wasn't the right word. Rosendale wasn't really a cult. He didn't know everything, even though he thought he did. He never was out of Easton in his whole life. Cults had leaders with super powers, but not Rosendale. There were just friends at Rosendale, and so many of them. So she left him in his own blessed office, in his own blessed Easton, and she went along with the others. She did it. By herself. Without his approval. In spite of his "concern."

When she felt the blizzard cold at her fingertips, she pulled on her gloves. But this storm business was all too much like a story, or a joke—the traveling salesman jokes. At least she knew where she was, and she knew Jiggs Dekker, or knew of him, living back there in the house at the corner. She couldn't see the place in the mirror, but she knew it was there because it always had been the house on Poodles Corner, attached to the old DX station.

The wind scooped the door open when she twisted out of the Mustang, and the blowing snow brushed her face like a fine ratchet. At least she knew where she was. In her whole life she had never said a word to Jiggs Dekker, but she knew he once ran the DX, and she knew that all of Easton thought Jiggs was a bit on the eccentric side, but such a lovable character.

Anyway, she was only three miles from town. Easton, and her stepfather, were just over the hill.

She walked bootless in the tracks the Mustang had cut through the snow minutes before. It might be hours before the plows would get to a road like this; it was the highways first during bad storms. In a half hour the car would be drifted in by the snow that seemed to streak along the ground, to rise up from the long drifts, from the earth, like the flood, Noah's flood.

A light from Jiggs' window flashed in the haze of snow like some metallic apparition. She grabbed the neck of the coat with her right hand and tried to breathe into her glove, her face lowered away from the snow, all the while tightroping on the track left by her car. She couldn't help thinking of the Mustang—how quiet it would be there, alone and cold. She tightened her lips as if to protect them, and she glanced up at the light, cut and fractured by the snow in her eyes, as if she were looking through the trifocals of some woman too old to see anything clearly. It was still too much like a story, getting trapped like this in a blizzard.

He came to the door the fourth time she knocked and his oddly pointed face seemed almost reassured.

"It's a darn strange thing that you're out there on a night like this, woman," he told her.

"My name is Kathy," she said, "Kathy Verhaalen. Konrad Brethhower is my stepfather."

Her let her in, smiling.

She wouldn't have guessed that anyone this close to Easton would dare keep house like Jiggs Dekker. The place was piled with paper, like a library workroom. Green plants—ivys, philodendrons, sprawling ferns—spread out over the living room and webbed the stacks of papers and magazines. An unlit Coca-Cola clock hung from a flower-papered wall, the minute hand broken, the stubbier hour hand pointing out the same hour it had been showing for what was obviously a long time. The place made her afraid of him in a way; it was as if she couldn't know this man, as if a man who lived this way wasn't really from her father's Easton. But he didn't say much when she asked him if she could use his phone.

"Calling somebody'd be a thoughtful thing to do," he told her. "I think you'll find it just about directly under that sign there."

"My Mind To Me An Empire Is," the sign read. She wondered how she could have missed seeing it when she came in the door. She glanced back at him from the hallway. He was an ugly man with short hair. He sat in a big maroon easy chair covered by some ancient tapestry. From the moment she came in, she thought he acted too much as if this was some kind of social call. But he was only lovable Jiggs Dekker. Everybody in Easton knew Jiggs Dekker. Countless times she'd seen him herself on the street downtown.

She found the phone beneath a tiffany lamp. "I'm at Poodles Corner—you know, at Mr. Dekker's," she told her stepfather.

She could picture him nodding just a bit like he always did when she told him something he didn't want to hear. Something that "concerned" him.

"We'll figure something out," he told her. "Are you okay, Kathy?"

"Oh, don't be ridiculous," she said. "It's not like I'm trapped in the city or something." With her left hand she thumbed through a stack of *Life* magazines from the '40s—covers of planes and men in uniforms.

"Well, you don't have to give it a thought," he said. "We'll work something out all right—don't worry." It was a way he had of using *we,* as if he were speaking for some committee. There was no one else since her mother had died years ago.

Jiggs' thick legs angled across each other like two thick sticks of sausage. "Now, who are you again?" he said, shifting his weight to the other side of the chair when she came back to his front room. The tapestry draped from a top corner, revealing stuffing the color and texture of dirty wool.

"My stepfather is Konrad Brethhower," she said, laughing. "You must know him."

"Certainly, certainly."

He looked almost offended. His gray, perfectly circular face puckered into firm resolution. His lips were red like very good salmon, thick at the center. He looked as though he were constantly inhaling an invisible cigarette, politely, at the points of his lips. She didn't know whether or not to call him Jiggs, but she had no idea what his real name might be.

"Do you think I could stay here, Mr. Dekker? I mean, it's not likely I could get home tonight anymore."

"Of course you can stay. I was planning on it already. Not much is going to happen out there tonight." He leaned over as if to look out of the curtained windows to check the storm. She saw his hairless leg, white as chalk, when his trousers twisted above his sock. "Your father won't make it out anymore tonight," he said, "not unless he's got a team, but there ain't no more teams in Easton to my knowledge. Nope." He leaned back and smiled almost

257

pleasantly, she thought. "And by the way, you might think of just calling me Jiggs like everybody else does. It's what I been going by for more'n forty years already." He stopped, looked down, as if to make a deliberate pause. He wriggled his finger in his ear. "Brethhower's daughter you are?" he said.

"Konrad Brethhower," she said, "but my name is Kathy —Kathy Verhaalen." She hated repeating her stepfather's name like that, but she knew Jiggs could file her into an Easton family that way. She wouldn't be just any old straggler in from the storm. "It's my own dumb fault for running out of gas. Never thought of it. Stupid of me."

"You might enjoy a cup of tea maybe?" he said. "Just happened to be boiling some water this minute when you came in." He rubbed his hand over his head as if to make his short hair stand up in the old style brush cut.

"I would—"

"It ain't that I get visitors all the time, you know. I'm sure a little rusty on my manners."

She watched his squat body disappear into the kitchen. It was almost frog-like—thick in the middle—except for the heavy legs.

The place was what she always imagined a rabbit's den might look like, little ruts swept through the rubbish —paper things of all kinds. There was a space around his favorite chair and a path out to the kitchen, a kind of clearing around a southern window. The river flats were out there, she knew; she guessed he might like to stand there and look out over the farms and the woods that followed the tangling waterway through the fields. Otherwise, it was a mess, mostly second- and third-class mail, colorful ads for magazine subscriptions and overseas travel, coupon books, catalogs and advertising circulars, all kinds and sizes. It wasn't pretty. She wound her left foot around her right leg. Leaning against the far wall was a tagboard female with huge breasts pulled together by a halter out of the forties, some kind of round things like rubber sealers still hooked to the ad at the bottom. She sat in her chair, motionless, her hands folded in front of her, elbows in at her sides.

But he made good tea. He balanced a cup and saucer on the arm of his chair, sat, and then rose again, his knees cracking like old twigs, then found a stereo somewhere amid the stacks of stuff. When she heard Vivaldi she noticed the speakers on the ceiling. She saw him watching her, waiting for her to show some surprise or appreciation for his miraculous providence.

The music was beautiful. She nodded politely, like her stepfather might have. She was thankful that she hadn't worn a skirt.

Silence had never been comfortable for her. It reminded her of herself, and it had always made her nervous. She could feel silence stretch through her stomach and her fingers.

"So how long has it been since you quit the station?" she said.

Her question didn't appear to register. Jiggs' cheeks jumped up and down and he squinted at her as if she spoke some foreign language. "Sorry," he said, "I'm still trying to tune you in."

"I said—'When did you leave the station?'"

"Never left it at all. It's same as always right out that door." He pointed with his thumb over his right shoulder.

"I mean, when did you run it last?"

"Twelve years ago, come November."

She thought it was a strange way of saying it—"come November"—as if November were next month, but she smiled at him. He sat there studying her. It was beginning to appear that she bore responsibility for the conversation. He wore that strange puckered smile constantly. It seemed to insist that the whole thing, even the conversation, had been planned out for weeks.

But this was only Jiggs Dekker sitting here, she told herself, the Jiggs Dekker who lived just west of Easton for as long as she could remember. Somehow he surprised her. His eyes twitched nervously, the kind of blinking one does to get out dust.

"It's not that I don't work, you see. Oh no, it's not that at all." He smiled a polite but poorly practiced smile. "Maybe you'd like to see my shop. I make these things

259

here," he said, pointing up at the wall near the kitchen. "Nothing Is At Last Sacred But The Integrity Of Your Own Mind." The quotation was burned into a perfectly white square of wood, heavily varnished to a glossy shine. The hand was graceful, stylish, 19th century, decorated with elegant squiggles.

"You did that?" she said.

"Certainly. You mean to say you wouldn't figure a guy like me could do something that pretty?"

"It's not that at all," she said. "I didn't mean it that way." She tried to laugh to cover her embarrassment. She put down her tea and walked over to the plaque. "It's really very nice. Where did you ever learn to print like that? You must be an artist."

"It's just something that I always had in me. Don't know where it come from originally. Just natural with me. You ought to see where I work. Just take the cup of tea along down. I got to show you what I got down here." It was almost a command, and she knew she was in no position to deny him. She heard the wind outside, Vivaldi's nervous violins within.

His basement was his real world, clean, controlled, lit brilliantly, almost as if the sun itself was charging through all the rubbish of the sitting room. The tools lined up along the bench, precisely, conveniently. The opposite wall was hung with several of his latest: "For They Can Conquer Who Believe They Can"; "Who Would Be Free, Themselves Must Strike the Blow," and a long one; "Happiness Is That Something Still For Which We Bear To Live Or Dare To Die."

"What do you think?" he said.

She touched them, each one of them. "You make them from scratch?" She ran her fingers lightly over the surface of the biggest one, trying to feel for the lines in the grain.

"Everything but the words. This here's my Bible." He pointed with his tea cup to a *Bartlett's Familiar Quotations.* "How do you like them?"

"They are very nice. Do you sell them?"

"Once in awhile."

"They are really beautiful, Jiggs. You know that—they

260

are very, very nice."

"Lots of people really take to 'em. Here, let me grab your cup. I got more brewing upstairs."

Dekker's basement was something like Rosendale, something like it. She listened to his footsteps up the stairs behind her. There were always signs there with words like these. And everyone believed them, of course. And they were all constantly quoting them to each other, as if they might forget otherwise, as if none of them dared to forget. But it was more than that. They all believed those words too, and when you said them to each other—"God is Love," or "Trust and Obey"—when you shared those things with someone else, someone close, someone who believed like you did about it all, it made you feel like you really belonged there, like you belonged to someone. It was words that made it so easy to hug the others. And it wasn't hard at all, not with words like that. Just a line and you could stand outside on North Dakota street corners and peddle flowers all day. Just a few words. That's all. It didn't seem like it was all that much, but it was amazing what words could do.

There they were, up on the wall before her. She felt as if she were standing before a whole library of books opened up to her alone. Words like that made people you didn't even know seem close as brothers or sisters. They made it easy to stand up to her father the way she had. It wasn't difficult. She knew Rosendale wasn't at all like Easton. But he never understood that. That's why he had taken her back from North Dakota.

"I thought that maybe a girl like you would like them." It was as if Jiggs hadn't left her alone down there. He stood behind her with her cup full of tea, and she had a strange feeling that he had been looking in through the back of her head.

"I think I got you now. You're the one that was out West somewhere in the cult-like thing, weren't you?" he said, pushing the cup into her hands.

"How did you know?"

"Big news in town. Shoot, there wasn't a soul around Easton didn't know all about it. You was the only one in town that got themselves mixed up in junk like that. When did you leave that place?"

But Jiggs didn't know the whole story. Maybe Easton didn't know it either—how her stepfather had grabbed her one night, had stolen her from the family at Rosendale.

"You don't know, do you?" she said.

When she looked at him, she felt him waiting to be told.

"My stepfather took me out—did you know about that?"

He never stopped smiling. "Must've been hell itself," he said. He stayed where he was. She heard him breathe, a slight whistling sound.

"Wasn't hell over there—not at all." She stepped behind a bench, keeping it between them. "It wasn't hell. I suppose Easton would say that places like Rosendale are hell." She pulled the cup up to her lips with both hands. "I suppose that's what people would say here, but if you ask me, sometimes I think that Easton is hell." She looked away to cover her shame with anger, then turned back toward him and stared. "You must know what I mean, Jiggs."

Jiggs' smile spread through his pursed lips. He picked up a board from the bench and blew off the sawdust.

"But I don't want to talk about it," she said.

"Why don't you just get out of here and go back if it's so good out there," he said, "if that's what you want?" His eyes were not so hard as she had thought at first. In the strong fluorescent light of the basement, his eyes seemed calm enough, committed, almost confident—blue, comfortable eyes.

"It's not that I haven't thought of it—of leaving again."

"You don't owe no dues to Easton, you know. No sir. Old enough already to take care of your own soul; take it and run if that's what you want." His eyes twitched steadily. "I suppose your old man is always watching over you."

She stepped back and rested against the side of the workbench, beneath the finished plaques, and she put the cup down firmly on the bench.

"How do you do it, Jiggs?" she said.

"What's that?"

"I mean, how do you live here, in the middle of this place—Easton, I mean?"

"Don't think I do live in the middle of this place. Nope. I don't belong to Easton and Easton don't belong to me." When he laughed, she smiled along with him. "I just live out here by myself and don't bother no one. Easton just happens to be right down the road a ways."

"You just live here and make these things," she said.

"Just turn out some of these wall plaques to sell come Christmas. People buy 'em uptown at the florist shop. Put 'em up on their walls at home, I guess. Some of 'em don't probably. Some buy 'em because they feel sorry for the crazy old man who lives down at Poodles Corner making plaques." He laughed in a kind a grunt. "You don't owe no dues to this place or anybody in it, dear," he said.

She reminded herself that she had never really known this Jiggs Dekker, known of him but never really known the man. His constant pucker ironed itself out when he smiled at her the way he did.

"How about it—you want to make one of these yourself?" he said. "Got a short one here all ready for you. Printed up this one this afternoon, matter of fact. Won't take no time at all. You can do one this size in just a couple of minutes." He reached back under the counter and pulled out a thin pine board, perfectly white, the size of a cigar box cover. Its edges were already notched up and down the sides to make it look as if it were broken off the plank it came from. "What do you say? Got nothing else to do tonight and all the time in the world to do it."

A thin coat of white dust made the board's surface slightly scratchy.

"Look here," he said, motioning her over to his side, beneath the brim of light from the bench. "See these lines right on here? I penciled 'em in real light. All you got to do is follow them lines with this tool here—won't take a second to get the sucker heated up. That's all there is—and you got yourself a plaque. Made it yourself. Course we got to varnish it up some yet, but we can start on that too tonight. Ain't nothing going to be interrupting us with that blizzard howling outside."

She could barely make out the faint lines. "Custom Is The Law Of Fools," it said. She smiled to see it all finally. It was just like the other, the letters flowing into one another. It was really pretty.

"Just try it once," he said, poking the instrument at her.

"What do you call that?"

"Just the woodburning tool is all. Gets a little hot down there around the end," he pointed at the end, black as charcoal, "but you ain't got to touch it down there anyway. Just hold it right here on the cork and draw them letters in."

She took it from him carefully, like a surgeon might.

"You don't have to be scared of that thing. It ain't going to hurt you at all. Nothing more than a hot pencil."

She smiled at him. It was thicker than a pencil of course, and she could feel its warmth beneath the cork collar. And it was heavy. She put it between her fingers and wiggled it in the air as if she were already writing.

"That's it," he said. "That's all there is to it."

She looked back at him.

"Go on and try it," he said. He rubbed his palm over his head, and the short hair on his crown stood for a second. "Won't hurt you none. You can take it along when you leave in the morning."

She brought the angled point down to the clean white wood and poked it at the top of the *C*.

"Just go on and put it down there. You'll see how quick it burns."

In a second she saw the brown scar grow out from the point of the pencil. She pulled it toward her, following Jiggs' patterned *C*.

"That's it. That's good. That's really fine, you know that?"

She pulled it along slowly, watching the path she cut behind the point and the fine lines of the pencil-marked pattern.

"Now just a little harder on there. Little more with the wrist." He put his hand on hers and pushed down lightly. The scar widened to a quarter inch. "Oh, that's just wonderful, girl," he said. "That's it. Got to be able to see it from a distance. Plaque ain't worth nothing if people can't read what it's supposed to say."

She pushed harder when he released his grip, and she felt her wrist quiver from the constant strain when she went on to the small *u*. "Nothing to it," she said.

"That's pretty darn good what you done there. That's really pretty darn good. You got yourself a steady hand there. Hands of an artist, you got. You and me better start us a big business. Start selling them things in the big city." He laughed from behind her and she let up for a minute to turn and acknowledge his joke, grinning herself.

"Can I do the whole thing?"

"Better not quit once you started. You're doing real good—go on."

It wasn't all that hard. She found herself enjoying it. She could tell by the looseness in her wrist that she'd have to build up a muscle or two, but when she looked back at what she'd done, she saw her lines were really very smooth and curved, no breaks anyway, and the quarter inch thickness followed along quite consistently. The fine smell of burning wood came up directly into her nostrils. It was sharp and clean, like the fires they built every night out at Rosendale, big fires, heavenly fires, the center of everybody's attention, marshmallow-singing-sharing fires. She finished the *m*, pulling the hot pencil along in one even motion.

"Now just take a look at that," Jiggs said. "That's just as fine as I could have done myself, I swear. You're just a natural, dear."

She took a step back like an artist. "It does look really good," she said. "I have to admit it myself." She told him with her eyes that the work was good.

"Now don't be holding your face so close to the iron, girl. Your cheeks is starting to get a blush on them," he said.

She giggled like a child.

When she heard the baritone voice from up the stairs and the sound of footsteps over the floor, she jammed the woodburner back in Jiggs' hand and slid to the side of the bench, away from the steps. "It's him," she said. "It's my stepfather again. I'm sure it's him. How could he have made it out here?"

"Probably ain't nothing to sweat. Probably some other driver got stuck in the snow." He jerked the plug from the socket and set the woodburner down quietly on the bench.

"I'm sure it's him. I heard his voice."

"You don't have to be afraid of nothing, dear. Here now, just tell him to get lost if you ain't interested in leaving with him. Maybe he just come to check up on you or something. He's your father, ain't he? Ain't nothing to be scared of." He nudged her forward from behind, his hands clamped on her arms, and when she turned her head, she saw the same proud puckered smile and the twitching eyes.

"I don't want to go, Jiggs," she said. "He doesn't have to be taking me away all the time. I've got my own life to live."

"You don't have to do nothing you don't want to do. This here's a free country." He had a firm hold of her arms, and he kept steering her toward the bottom of the stairs. "If you ain't interested in going along with him, just tell him so. Go on. What's he to you? Girls like you has got to learn you don't belong to no one. Go on."

"Anybody here?"

She heard his voice again. She couldn't guess how he had made it out here in the storm. But he was always there—just like that night in North Dakota, in the motel room, in the dark. She had known he was there with her the second she came in alone. She could feel his presence like a shadow hanging over her, some looming presence simply forever there.

She had refused to leave with him then, but his face bore down at her, emotionless, it seemed, intense, his head nodding just slightly when he walked out of the darkness of the back of the room.

"You're all right?" he had said that night.

When she turned to run, he ran to slam the door shut in front of her. He stood there before her—tall, exact, his features barely visible in the flashing reds of neon from the sign outside the motel window.

First she had kicked at him; she slapped him; she swore. But he had grabbed her then, his huge hands clamped on her arms, firmly, gently, holding her up like some ballerina, her legs flailing, her neck twisting sideways, backwards, when she tried to bite his iron hands, his shoulders. To Easton he had taken her.

"I'm sorry you don't like it," he had said later, miles away, "but I'm taking you back. I can't stand to see you doing this to yourself." Then he had added, as if he knew she wouldn't believe him, but felt he had to say it, "It's really best, Kathy." But what did he know?

She reached back and put her left hand on Jiggs' hip to reassure herself of his presence this time.

"Go on and do it," Jiggs said. "Tell him where to get off." They stood directly beneath him at the bottom of the stairs. "He don't own you. Just tell him to get lost and leave you alone."

She saw her stepfather standing there at the top, big as a vision, and she saw his legs, his hips, his chest in the semi-darkness. And in her mind she saw his face, his sickening, handsome face, his eyes, his dark brown eyebrows so perfect, so symmetrical, the face her mother had somehow loved.

"Kathleen, is that you?" he said. "Is my daughter down there, Jiggs?"

"Nobody owns you," Jiggs told her. "Tell him as much."

"I'm here to take you home, Kathy," her stepfather said.

"Go on, tell him to get out. Go on and do it. Go on—"

She felt her arms drop when Jiggs let her go and jumped out from behind her. He stood at the base of the stairs, bent over at the waist to see the figure at the top. "Go on home, Brethhower. She ain't no more your daughter than she is mine," he yelled, his voice cracking.

"Kathleen, you down there? Are you all right?" His voice seemed to her untroubled, emotionless. She watched his boots descend the steps. Snow laced the creases in his trousers like a thick white dust, and his black jacket hung open and loose. When she looked in his eyes she remembered him slapping her face as she struggled with him in the car outside the North Dakota motel. It was over then, all her fighting. She wanted him angry now. She wanted to hurt him for always being there.

"Why don't you just go back to your blessed Easton," she said. "Just stay out of my life for once." She was powerless to staunch her tears.

"That's it, that's it!" Jiggs prodded. "More of that!"

But he simply stood there, one hand on the rail, speechless, his dark eyes trained on her as if they were magnetized. She tried to look away.

"Kathy, it's okay now," he said assuringly. "I won't leave without you. I've got some gas on the snowmobile. We can get you out. Come along now."

"She ain't coming." Jiggs brought his finger up to the dark man's face. "Why don't you just take your blessed snowbuggy back where it come from and let this girl alone? This here is my house, and you ain't got a right in the world to come blowing in here as if you own it. Who do you think you are anyhow?"

He kept staring at her, as if Jiggs wasn't even there. His dark eyes were warm, but somehow she wanted to refuse him.

"I'm her father," he said. When he pulled off his cap, melted snow fell from the wool and spotted the workroom floor. "My word, Jiggs, what's got into you?"

"Seems to me that she's rejected you, Brethhower. You got to be a blind man not to see." Jiggs came back to her and put a hand under the hair at the back of her neck. "This here look like the face of somebody who wants you to be watching over her all the time? This here looks more like rejection to me. Look—she don't need you no more. She don't even want you."

"Take your hand off my daughter, Jiggs," he said. He walked over to her and all three stood together.

"Can't you see this face? Look here. Look close. She don't want you. Let her live her own life. She really looks like she wants you, doesn't she?"

"Don't do this, Jiggs," he said. "Take your hand off her."

"This ain't love carved in this face. Can't you see it?"

"Don't be standing between me and my daughter—"

"She ain't your daughter, Brethhower. She's as much my

daughter as she is yours. Just clear out and let this girl alone for one time in her life."

"Get out of my way, Jiggs."

"You get out of my house."

"Jiggs—"

The old man jostled him toward the stairs. "Get out and leave her be, Brethhower." But as the father pushed Jiggs aside, the old man's body twisted and his knees collapsed. He rolled like so much dead weight, until his hips caught on the front legs of the workbench, his arms splaying in a frustrated gesture.

When her father knelt at Jiggs' side, she ran up the stairs and through the stacks of rubbish. She swore to herself that she wouldn't have him, she wouldn't go back, he couldn't force her this time. She pulled her hands into fists when she pulled on her coat. The blizzard pounded in through the open front door, and everything outside seemed a sudden, lifeless blank. She stumbled down the front steps, her eyes nearly closed in the onslaught of snow, her vision gone through her tears.

And the snowmobile stood there long and black as a monster—clean, shiny clean, metallic, evil, untouched by the snow, as if it were somehow immune, the gas can still strapped to the back of the seat. She toweled the wet from her eyes with her coat sleeve, and she imagined his own dark reflection mirrored in the hood. So damned clean it was.

She wouldn't go back with him. He wouldn't take her back again.

She jerked the strap off and opened the can. He still wasn't behind her. She held the can chest-high and poured gas over the seat, over the hood, down into the engine. The snow turned dark where the gas spilled down at the sides of the machine. She glanced back at the house. Still she didn't see him at the door. The can grew lighter as it emptied, and the gas splashed down over everything. She threw it aside when the gas was gone.

Still crying, she searched her pockets for matches. The wind screamed, and the snow smacked hard into her face and hands. She turned back toward the house, away from

the wind, and struck the match, dropping it, lit, in the same motion.

Time slowed. She watched the yellow flame erupt from the seat and then, as if in slow motion, creep in long fingers over the spilled gas. And she watched it jump to her own feet, powerless to slap it off. She watched her coat break into flame, and she felt the heat snap up at her face. She spread her arms instinctively, aghast, as if she had been suddenly awakened in the robes of a queen.

He saw her there, a pillar of flame, and he shoved her down with both of his arms, then covered her with his body, the heavy blizzard snow in her mouth and nose, cold and wet. She felt his body on top of hers like some unyielding legacy, and she felt the cessation of wind when he formed a shelter over her with his arms.

"Kathy, I love you," he said. "You're my daughter, Kathy."

And when he carried her up, his arms around her, through tears she saw the childlike imprint of an angel in the snow.

The Last of the Frisians

Menno Brandsma thought he'd rather be dead than leave South Dakota for Arizona, even in January. He thought golf was as silly as grown men in short pants, and although he'd never have said it to his snowbird friends from Scrooby church, he thought it more than a little slothful to be sitting around in lawn chairs outdoors in the middle of winter.

But it was those Scrooby friends who wintered down in Arizona who told him about this man Al Young, spelled with a Y. Said he was Frisian, like Menno, and he had this one bad eye. Said they had a cup of coffee with him right there in Goldwater's store in a big Phoenix shopping mall. Met the man at some map display—a whole circle of guestbooks lettered with states' names in gold. Looked just like pew Bibles, they told Menno.

This man, Al Young, the Frisian, was just ready to scratch his name in the South Dakota book when he spotted their names—De Jong, Joldersma—right up there above the blank space. That's what got him talking, they said.

Later on, this Al Young (his real name was Aaldert Jongsma, they found out later) told them he had grown up with their own friend from Scrooby, Menno Brandsma. "He and I were kids together back in Witmarsum," he told them. They said he acted surprised that they might know someone he did from the old country. "That's so long ago," he kept saying. Hadn't seen his old friend Menno for sixty years, he told them—not since the Brandsmas immigrated. They told him Menno was doing just fine now, moved to town ten years ago already.

That was April—when the snowbirds came back to Scrooby because it was finally warm enough for their tender hides. Menno waited for the last risk of snow to pass because he couldn't trust himself driving the Impala on icy roads. This much he knew.

Three times it took him to get a call through to this man Al Young—and why would anyone change his name like that, such a perfectly good Frisian name? The third time he tried on Sunday morning, just before church in Scrooby, the time he was sure that his old friend Aaldert Jongsma would be tuned to "The Calvinist Hour of Praise" right there on KCLN in Sioux Falls, right there where he lived, not more than two hours away from Scrooby—east mostly, but a bit south, maybe five or six miles if you judged by the airport. Menno thought it was amazing that his old boyhood friend could have lived so close and for so many years in America.

"Aaldert, yeah, is that you?" he said when he heard the voice on the other end.

Just some breathing there was through the phone.

"Aaldert Jongsma, is that you there holding this phone?" he said.

"Yes, yes—this is. Who on earth is this?"

"Menno—your old friend Menno Brandsma from Witmarsum, from Friesland. You remember all right."

"Menno? Oh, Menno Brandsma—sure. Yes. I remember now. But how long has it been since I've talked to you—"

"I live here in Scrooby now—"

"Menno Brandsma, sure. Well, how are you, Menno? It's just so long—"

"Yeah, fine with me. Fine with me. And you?"

"Good, sure, sure. Real good. You know, Menno, just this last winter in Arizona I met some folks who knew you. From that little town—"

"Scrooby."

"Scrooby, yes, that's it. Odd name."

Scrooby was never such an odd name to Menno Brandsma.

274

"And those people told me they knew you. Wasn't that something? You know, if they hadn't talked about you, I probably wouldn't even remember your name right now. I mean, near to sixty years it's been, Menno."

"Sixty years. Amazing thing. Just this one wire connects us now, after so many years." Menno thought it was something just to stand there and think of it.

"What can I do for you, Menno?"

"Aaldert, you don't have on the radio?"

"Yes, I think so—let me listen once. Yes, it is."

"Not on 'The Calvinist Hour'—8:30, Sunday morning?"

"Pardon me?"

" 'The Calvinist Hour.' KCLN right there in Sioux Falls—the one with the big tower going west out of town past the airport. 'The Calvinist Hour.' "

"To be truthful, Menno, I'm not sure what the wife has on. I was just sitting here with the morning paper."

Nobody in Scrooby bought Sioux Falls papers on the Sabbath, it wasn't done. But Aaldert lived in the middle of secularism there in the city. That was something to remember too, of course.

"I thought maybe when the weather isn't so warm yet I could drive up to Sioux Falls and visit. You got coffee, Aaldert?"

"Call me Al, Menno. Long ago already I changed my name. Years ago in California."

"You lived in California?"

"Years ago. When we first came over. My father couldn't make it in Minnesota. We went to California after just a few months."

It was something to think of his old friend with the one bad eye living out there in California. Menno knew there were some good Frisians out there running some big dairies, but he always wondered how good Calvinists could hold the faith in all that California sin.

"So much there is to hear from my old friend," Menno told him. "When would it be good for me to come to Sioux Falls for coffee? Tuesday maybe?"

He could hear the music in the background, soft music—the kind they played in the grocery store. Cheap music, but not bad music.

"My wife says Tuesday's no good. How about Thursday, in the afternoon?"

Menno didn't like missing the Rook game at the Scrooby Cafe, even for Aaldert Jongsma. "Friday afternoon?" he said.

He heard Aaldert slip his hand over the mouthpiece. He wondered what an old man like Jongsma could be busy with anyway on a Tuesday.

"She says it's okay," he said.

Strange thing to always have to check with his wife. Menno wondered if he asked her when he could visit the toilet.

"You tell me where, Aaldert."

"Al," he said. "You just call me Al, Menno."

"In Sioux Falls I don't get around anymore so well. So much building going on there now. New roads and too many cars too. Where is it you live?"

Aaldert told him it was on the northwest side, a new suburb, a condominium right across the street from the new Presbyterian church. "Maybe you've seen that church in the paper. It has quite an original design."

Menno never missed the church news, last page of the first section every Saturday. "That one like a pup tent without a pole?"

"Maple Glen Presbyterian—that's the one."

"You can still walk to church, even in the city," Menno said.

"What's that?"

"I say you can walk to church, even in the city?" It wasn't as if Aaldert was so many miles away. Menno had to remind himself not to yell.

"Oh, yes, yes—we could walk to church," Aaldert said. "We live just across the street—11345 North Maple Hills—you can park right there in the street. Watch for the number," he said.

Menno knew a man in Wisconsin who had bought a farm and joined the Presbyterian church because there were no Dutch Reformed churches around. But Sioux Falls had three. Soon enough he'd find out why Aaldert

Jongsma had turned his back on his own church, he thought.

"Already this bill is too high, Aaldert. You know how it is with money when you get old. Friday we'll talk anyway."

"Friday—Friday afternoon."

Clarence and Darlene and Fred all lived around Scrooby. Johnny was killed in the war, of course, and the other children were gone here or there, most of them still in the Dakotas. Menno's wife, Alma, had died ten years before, so every Sunday after church one of the kids would have Menno over for Sunday dinner. Clarence and Audrey farmed a mile south and three west of town. Clarence told his father that driving in Sioux Falls was no picnic anymore. "Audrey likes to shop over in Sioux Falls," he said.

But Menno told them that Aaldert Jongsma gave him good directions. "And besides," he said, "you can't miss that big Presbyterian church that was written up in the church news."

"I'm always looking for an excuse to get away shopping, Dad," Audrey said.

But Menno said he had written down Jongsma's phone number. If he'd get lost somewhere, he could just give his old friend a call and find out where he was, he said.

So he left plenty early, just after coffee on Friday morning, and all the way up to the city he thought about those old times in Witmarsum, about being boys again, and he guessed at what Aaldert might look like today, sixty years later. Of course he lived in California for a time, and the wife and he went to that Presbyterian church across the street, they said—there in the new part of town. He might look different today, Menno thought.

And he didn't listen to "The Calvinist Hour" either. And he bought the Sunday paper. And his name was changed too. Menno smoothed over his bald head with the palm of his hand as he left Scrooby on the blacktop to the city.

One thing was sure. Aaldert Jongsma had that bad eye. That was the same yet for sure. Maybe they were six or seven years old, just boys when it happened. No, it was nine. They had left Friesland when he was ten, and it happened just before—maybe six months, during the winter. Every day they had played together then, the best of friends, always building things in the meadows and woodlands, sometimes grabbing sweet rolls from the Jongsma bakery, always laughing together.

One day they found this old stump in a clearing, just outside of town. All morning they worked to jerk it out, pulling and pushing at the rotten thing, playing like little boys, he and Aaldert. Maybe it wasn't right for them to try to get it out, Menno said—after all the stump wasn't their property. Aaldert said it was useless anyway, and Menno worried too much. Who wants a dumb old stump like this, he said. Of course, they talked Fries then, not English.

After lunch they brought back a long pole, a big pipe from Menno's barn. They shoved it underneath that old stump and then leaned on it until both pairs of feet came up off the ground. Just a little that old stump would budge. Maybe a half inch at a time. Very slow. So they jammed that pipe down deeper into the stump and leaned even harder, jerking it with more weight to try to pry that thing out. It was fun.

Aaldert leaned over the stump and tried to yank it. Big pieces of rotten wood broke off in his hands like clumps of wet sawdust. "Lower," Menno said, and Aaldert arched his back over the stump, digging his fingers into the rotten stuff.

"I'll pull here," Aaldert said, "and you jump on the pole." He pointed up at the end. "Now!"

Menno leaned over the pole. Aaldert jerked at the stump.

"Harder," Aaldert said.

So Menno jumped on the bar, curling his waist over it, his feet dancing off the ground. The sudden jerk nudged the pipe just enough to skip it out of its hold beneath the stump. Menno nearly fell when the pipe broke out, but the end shot upward and caught Aaldert's head full force. It was a bad sound, soft—a mushy sound. Aaldert never said a word, but when he looked up, he seemed surprised by what had happened. What Menno saw then he never forgot, of course—the eye falling in a liquid clump from its socket, like a broken egg. That was something—to see that eye there was something.

His friend Aaldert had a new glass eye already when the Brandsmas left for the new country.

So that much he knew. This Al Young still had one glass eye. That hadn't changed.

The city was stretched out almost to the airport now. Menno couldn't remember the last time he'd been there—maybe two years ago, maybe more. It was still before noon when he found the odd church, so he went back a mile or so to a Hardware Hank and bought, on sale, several yards of that red outdoor carpet for his front steps. Menno couldn't get it that cheap in Scrooby. He thought it would be nice to tell his friends at the cafe how cheap he got it in Sioux Falls. The rest of the time he just looked around the store at all the stuff. Next door was a Dairy Queen, so he had a vanilla cone—as long as he was parked so close anyway.

Scrooby had no condominiums, but he knew what they were—just little homes jammed together in one big house. He'd never seen them before, really, except in the papers. When he drove back to the church, he realized it would take a good hunt to find Aaldert's. Maybe a hundred of them there were across that street. All of them in houses that looked pretty much alike—two doors far to the right and two far to the left, separated by garage space.

The streets were worse than silly, Menno thought. They curled in and around until you couldn't tell where you were going or where you had been before. Every place had four numbers on the front door. The only way he kept his bearings was by that ugly new church. Everything else looked alike. He thought it was a funny way to live—in coops.

He couldn't find 11345, so he thought he'd just have to ask. "Al Young." He kept repeating the name to himself. "I got to ask for Al Young because none of his neighbors know his real name."

He turned up toward a house and knocked on the door furthest toward the church. Then he saw the doorbell in a fancy web of molded metal, something shaped like the round teeth of a rotary hoe. Nobody came. He tried the bell. Nobody was home. So he tried the next door, just another step to the right. He figured people who lived this way—on top of each other—probably would want to be gone from home as much as they could. He figured this was what some people called a bedroom community. They didn't really mean what you might think when they said it either.

People said folks in Holland lived on top of each other, he remembered. Some Dutchmen visiting Scrooby relatives told him once how everybody had to ask the government if they could even put a room on a house in the old country. Of course it was all socialist now after the war. The whole country. That's what people said—everybody packed together like this in little buildings. Just wasn't the same anymore, people said. Some Scrooby folks went on tours to the old country. That's what they said too.

He hit the bell again on the third door.

When the door cracked open, he knew right away it wasn't Al Young. The man had two good eyes and he was way too young—maybe forty or so.

"Who you looking for?" the man said.

"Jongsma—Aaldert Jongsma," Menno told him, trying to lean his face to the same angle as the man's.

"Never heard of him."

"Lives here, he says."

"Not in this one." The man peeked out through a gap in the door and fiddled with the lock chain.

"You don't know him?" Menno said.

"What's his name?"

"Jongsma—ach, Al Young. Goes to that church over there."

The man's dark hair fell over his ears in clumps. "Don't know anyone who goes there anyway," the man said. "Check the numbers out there—out in front." Then he pushed the door shut and clicked the bolt. Menno wondered if the man was a hoodlum.

There were numbers on the lawn, something like street signs. He hadn't seen them before, but he thought missing them wasn't his fault because he never would have thought to look on somebody's lawn for directions. Didn't even allow people to put up House for Sale signs on your lawn in Scrooby. Cluttered up the town, people said.

A woman came to the door when he knocked at 11345.

"So this is the man," she said. "You must be Brandsma." Menno thought her face looked pinched. She didn't look like the wife of anyone he knew. She wore a gold necklace and a bright scarf around her neck, as if she was still a heifer, and her dark hair had too much red in it to be real—red mixed in with gray like the side of a barn.

If it weren't for the eye, he wouldn't have recognized Aaldert Jongsma. He wore his hair long and parted in the middle, like those handsome men on posters in the barber shop. Already when Menno married his wife, Alma, fifty years ago, he was bald.

"Menno," he said, "from Friesland."

"Scrooby," Menno said.

When Aaldert walked over to the door, Menno thought he moved like he was still fifty. His hand pumped good and strong. There they stood, shaking hands and just looking at each other until Menno thought it was already too long to carry on like that, two grown men. Aaldert's eye was hardly noticeable, Menno thought.

"That eye looks real good now. Just like the other one," he said.

"Back in here it's hooked," Aaldert said, pointing in his head, "and we bought this one color-coded. Supposed to work that when the good one moves, this one does too. Almost ten years already I had this one here."

"Miracles of modern medicine," Menno said. "cost you a fortune, I suppose."

"And how about you, Menno—you healthy?" Aaldert pointed him over to the couch, and Menno sat behind the flat stump with a varnished top that they set for a coffee table.

"My wife already was gone in '72, but the doctor says I'm tough as scrub oak. 'Menno,' he says, 'you got the body of a sixty-year-old man,' he says last checkup. Ten years I think I got yet." Aaldert looked familiar, but nothing else seemed comfortable. You had to sit with your legs straight out in front of you in such a place. There were long curtains on the windows and big pictures on the walls and fancy little statues all over—expensive things, standing on glass. Menno thought the whole place was a little fancy, the kind of place where you don't know if you can really breathe easy.

"Retired, I suppose?" Aaldert said.

"Sure, just a year before Alma died we moved to town. Some said it's what killed her, you know—moving away from the farm like that. But I know better. She never said nothing when I said to move. She never liked the farm that much."

"Never sick either?"

"You mean me?" Menno said.

"Always healthy?"

"Two years ago I was here in Good Samaritan, laid up with kidney stones. That's no picnic—terrible pain, you know. But the Lord delivered me that time. They got me on the bed, all shaved—all of this—" He ran his hand down his belly, stretching back. "Doctor says it won't be bad. 'We'll get that thing, Menno,' he says. Nice young kind—Italian. Catholic. Dark-haired boy. But right away before I go in, I told that nurse, I says, 'Maybe I got to visit the stool yet,' So she says, 'You do that.' And what do you know—ploop, out comes the stone. Just like that. And then the whole operation is off, and they send me back to Scrooby. Amazing thing."

Menno thought Aaldert's wife looked as if there was a fishbone caught in the back of her throat. But when Aaldert laughed, he looked even more familiar. Menno couldn't understand why anyone so old as Jongsma would wear his hair so long, as if he was still a kid.

"So all of you still works, Aaldert?" he said.

"My husband's name is changed to Al," his wife said.

"Maybe to you," he said, "but not to me."

"It's nothing major yet with me. You know how it is when you get to be seventy—here and there you get a pain."

"What's your wife's name?" Menno said.

"I'm so sorry, dear," Aaldert said. He got up from the chair and stood beside her. "This is Flora, Menno. Maybe when you have been married so long you just think that everyone who knows you, knows your better half."

Menno's Alma was a good wife, but Menno would never have called her his better half. Even Alma would have thought such a thing to be silly, almost like making fun.

"You're the man around here," she said to her husband.

Menno didn't know why, but he nodded.

"So who is the artist, Mrs. Jongsma? Is it you or this man you call Al Young?" Right over the dining room table was a big black and white, life-sized portrait of Franklin Delano Roosevelt, wheelchair and all, a cigarette holder in his lips. And that ugly wife of his behind him, the liberal—if you even want to call them husband and wife, Menno thought. Just about every wall had a picture of a president, all democrats.

"These are all my work. Truman, Kennedy too. I drew them from pictures in magazines." Aaldert pointed around. Harry Truman seemed ready to walk down the path in the picture and step right out on the floor of the living room. Kennedy sat at his desk on the wall near the bedroom, a kind of sad smile on his face.

"You do good work, Aaldert. Right away I can recognize all of these." He pointed across the room. "This one is Roosevelt, of course, and that is Truman from Missouri—the man used to swear too much, you know, and that one is Kennedy, the Catholic. Terrible thing what Oswald did. But they say he was warned—'Don't go to Dallas,' someone told him. But he went anyway. All of them Kennedys are headstrong."

"This country's never recovered from that. He was the only real leader for years." Menno thought Aaldert looked far too serious when he said such a foolish thing. There he sat looking down at the floor as if he was still mourning.

283

"Maybe you should draw the Pope right in there peeking over his shoulder—like Eleanor there," Menno said. He thought it was a good joke.

Flora said it was a terrible thing to say.

"I meant it funny," Menno said.

Aaldert leaned over toward his wife. "You know how they are, Flo," he said.

Menno thought he was talking about Catholics.

"I'm a democrat," Jongsma said. "The first time I voted was in '32." He pointed at Roosevelt. "For me there was no choice, was there? Roosevelt fed our family, Menno. He kept us alive during the Depression. I'll die a democrat."

Menno thought his old friend's language was a little strong for a subject that wasn't religious, but Menno usually said the country would be better off without so many democrats.

"You care for coffee, Mr. Brandsma?" Flora said.

"Yeah, maybe a bit early yet, but it would be good." He squinted at his watch. "It's a long ride here from Scrooby."

"This is all new—the church and down the street the shopping plaza, these apartments and condos," Aaldert said. "You found us all right?"

Menno laughed. "Maybe a little trouble," he said. He looked back over his shoulder. "But what is this plaque here—'Odd Fellows' and your other name—with a Y. You're an odd fellow, Aaldert—is that a joke?" He stood to read the words on the plaque.

"It's something like a club I belong to," Aaldert said.

Flora brought the coffee and some store-bought wind-mill cookies on a glass plate. Menno had never before drank coffee from a transparent cup.

"Cream or sugar?" she asked.

"Of course, cream." He took a teaspoon of powder. "Some of the children laugh about the cream," he said, stirring it in, "but they don't know good Frisians drink cream with coffee."

Flora poured her husband a cup black, then left him one cookie before going back to the kitchen. "So who are these odd fellows?" Menno said. He didn't bother asking why Aaldert took no cream.

284

"You've never heard of them? We're all over the country."

The way Aaldert crossed his legs, way down on the end of his knees, reminded Menno of a gentleman. "We have no odd fellows in Scrooby," he said.

"In California already I was a member. Out there there's a lot of Odd Fellows—"

"That sure is the truth—"

"It's a service club—raises money for hospitals and charities—good work."

Aaldert didn't seem to think his jokes were funny.

"Your people call it a lodge," Aaldert said.

Menno wasn't sure what "your people" meant, but he knew he didn't have any friends who belonged to a lodge, because he knew the church stood dead against it. He wondered what that woman, Flora, had done to his old friend, making him join a secret society.

"And these are your children, I suppose—only two?" he said, standing, pointing at the picture. "Both of them in the church?"

"Gary and Margaret. Both married, with families."

"That's nice," Menno said. He thought they looked quite normal. He watched his coffee closely as he sat back down behind the varnished stump.

"So tell me, Jongsma—why is it you changed your name?"

"To American—I changed it to American."

That didn't seem to be any kind of reason to Menno Brandsma.

"Menno, maybe I should tell you how it is with me today. Years ago my father went to California—after we came here—like I told you on the phone—after we came to Minnesota—"

Menno looked over at Flora chewing on a cookie beneath Roosevelt. All those big democrats staring at him made him nervous.

"We left all the other Frisians and the other Hollanders. You stayed in that little town—"

"Scrooby."

"Yes, and you probably even still speak the old

285

language. To me it is somewhere lost behind me. That's fifty years ago. I am an American." He put his cup down on the saucer and seemed to want to salute. "I remember how your people think about things, but that's all way behind me now. Years ago already I stopped thinking like your people. To me that's all in the past—in Friesland."

"What do you mean when you say 'your people' all the time?"

"I mean like Scrooby—church people, so Dutch and all that. Years ago already I left—"

"It's just that easy, Mr. Al Young?" Menno poked a finger in his ear. "One day you decide, 'Well, tomorrow I will be somebody else'—and so the next day, just like a snake, you just shed the old skin. Now, born-again American. Like that?"

"My wife and I—"

"What's her name? Flora what?"

"Flora Cooper," he said.

"She was Presbyterian?"

Aaldert glanced over toward his wife as if trying to remember so long in the past. "I think she was. You were, weren't you, Flo?"

"Presbyterian—like my mother," she said.

Menno nodded. "Maybe you left your people for her people—like Ruth. Last year we had in church a series on Ruth. Everything she gave up just for Naomi. Not even Jewish, and then she is the grandma of David himself."

Menno waited for Flora to nod her head or something, but the woman sat there smoothing her skirt over her legs.

"It wasn't just Flora, Menno. It's another world in this country—another world. When you come here, something you have to leave behind," he said.

He knew Aaldert was right, of course. Roosevelt himself was a Hollander.

"Your people say that Al married an American," she said. Menno guessed she thought it was a joke by the way she laughed about it. Anyway, he thought she was too small for a good wife.

"My Darlene married an American," he said. "Good boy too." He thought Flora might like that.

"Then you know," Aaldert said.

Menno nodded, but he wasn't sure what it was he was supposed to know.

"It was hard for Flo," Aaldert said, "hard for her to get along with your people."

"They wouldn't accept me, because I wasn't like them," she said. "They were so narrow. Your people are so narrow."

He knew that somehow she had insulted him. He decided to hate Flora. She wore dark stockings, but underneath he could see veins in her legs. "You remember Esau, Aaldert," he said. "He sold his birthright for some hot soup."

Flora's neck turned the same bright color as her scarf. "You can't live in the past, you know. Sooner or later you have to become Americans."

"You think maybe I'm Russian or what?" he said.

That reddish color squeezed up into her cheeks.

"Menno, in Scrooby everybody is Frisian, aren't they?" Aaldert said.

"And Hollanders—more Hollanders. And some others too—not many."

"Any Americans?"

"All of us Americans," Menno said. He put his see-through cup down on the stump. "My own son Johnny died in the war—over France. He was a flier with the army—my son was. So what does it mean to be an American then? Is it enough what I gave already? What must you be?" He jerked at his tie. "Do I have to be like you two—skim milk?"

"You going to let him talk that way in my house, Allan?" She growled like a dog around a fresh litter of pups.

"I didn't know you lost a son," Aaldert said.

"Already it's almost thirty years ago," Menno said.

"Allen, he called us 'skim milk'!" She uncrossed her legs and leaned toward her husband.

"How many other children, Menno?"

"Eight. Johnny I buried already—a good boy, serious. All the rest of them too. All of them. Johnny's last letter, I

287

have it yet. Sometime you can read it. What a testimony—
you bet, and on the last night before he died he wrote that
letter. All through them weeks when we didn't know about
our boy, Alma never once cried—not once. So sure we
were where Johnny was."

"Allen!"

Menno knew she would never understand them, not
when they started talking religion. Aaldert sat there nodding like a good dominie would have.

"So tell me, Aaldert, what kind of preaching do you get
there at that church?" Menno slid over to the left, closer to
his old friend.

Aaldert's lips kind of squirmed up under his nose. "What
do you mean?" he said.

"You know what I mean—in that strange church."

"We don't go to the Presbyterian church, Mr. Brandsma," Flora said. "Fact is, Al and I don't go to church at
all."

Menno felt something snap inside his chest, right above
his stomach. His jaw dropped open, but he seemed to have
no words.

"Last year I gave them a donation for that beautiful
building," his old friend said.

Menno wondered what it felt like to get a heart attack, if
it was anything like that—like someone with a mechanic's
fist just came up and grabbed all that stuff beneath the ribs
and squeezed. His jaw jerked up and he swallowed
hard—as if his mouth were full of potatoes.

"You know, sometimes—" Aaldert looked at his wife,
sitting there in front of Roosevelt. "I mean, I guess,
sometimes—not like never really—"

Menno put both hands on the couch and slowly brought
himself to his feet. "Maybe the Lord will forgive me for
what I think of your wife and you too," he said.

"You are the one who poked out my husband's eye," she
said. "For that I can never forgive the likes of you."

"You don't understand, Menno—"

"I won't have this man here any longer, Allan," she said.

"I'm leaving," Menno said.

Jongsma sat with both hands in his lap, his arms straight

down beside him.

"This man isn't Aaldert Jongsma anyway. Good thing he changed his name," Menno said. "And one more thing, woman," he said, "your coffee tastes like cheap bouillon."

"You don't understand, Menno. You been all your life in Scrooby," Aaldert watched his wife's eyes when he spoke. Menno thought it was meant for her, what he said.

He stood for a moment at the door. "Maybe I took this man's eye, but you took everything else and made him a gelding in the works."

Aaldert told him to leave.

He left the door open behind him, and heard their voices follow him down the steps. He hoped no one else was home to hear it. He dragged his feet in the grass outside, as if there were mud on his shoes.

Problem was it was too early to go back to Scrooby. People would wonder how Menno Brandsma could get back so fast from Sioux Falls and still have had coffee with his old friend, Aaldert Jongsma.

So he pulled the Impala over onto the shoulder right where the lanes bent around the airport runway—thought he'd watch a few planes come up off the ground.

He remembered the first time he had seen his own Johnny fly. It was like a miracle to think his own boy could do such a thing. Already it was years ago, of course, when the airport was just a little quonset. It was wartime then, and Johnny looked crisp and clean in that uniform, Alma said.

They had a proper burial in Scrooby, a stone and even a flag that the Legion Auxiliary changed every year in May. But Johnny's body never came back from France. Years ago already he used to think it must have been burned up completely, part of somebody's field.

He watched a passenger jet streak down the cement towards him, then saw its belly shine in the sun when it zoomed up over the Impala. He pushed his head out the window to watch it.

"Long ago already I left your people," this Al Young had told him. It was funny, how he thought that his own son

Johnny, dead in the war, never really did, even though his bones were never found.

But still there was that eye. He could write his old friend Aaldert a letter, he thought. He could write a letter to him yet because he knew the address. Maybe it would be best if it was in the Frisian language. Aaldert could walk to that ugly church.

Mason Tender

The problem of Dickie Vreeman belonged to our whole church, but Ed took it personally, because he had to deal with Dickie every day, and besides, to him, Dickie was family. Some people knew that Dickie had bad blood, because they knew his father had married this hard woman just before the war, and she left him one day with four kids—Dickie, the oldest—and all of that happened when no husbands and (certainly) no wives ever left, no matter what anybody suffered, because divorce was, to the whole village, unpardonable. Times change. But the people knew all of Dickie's problems weren't his own fault; he suffered himself on account of his real mother's bad blood.

Ed Vreeman took it personally because Dickie was his own brother's son, so years ago already Ed gave him a job as a mason tender, when Dickie moved back to town after a term in the reformatory and some rough times on his own. I suppose it was the good genes in the man that pushed him to work hard. Dickie took masonry seriously, and he worked like a beast for his uncle Ed, who was, at the time of the excommunication, a church officer. In a couple years Dickie knew everything there was to know about masonry.

By that time Dickie was no kid anymore either, even though he looked like one because he was so slim and dark from outside work. Dickie was already forty when the church decided to move against him once and for all, but he didn't look forty. When he peeled off his T-shirt, he'd show off that perfect, triangular chest, hair like fleece running up to his throat, as bleached as the thick hair on his head combed in the old duck-tail style. On hot days cement mix and dust stuck in his sweat and carpeted him. By July, with his lavender skin, he looked like a sage Negro. Proud veins lined the swollen muscles of his arms, but his wrists and his ankles were slight like a woman's. When he'd tote two full five-gallon buckets brimming with cement, when every inch of his upper body glistened with sweat, he could have been a model or a perfect naked statue in fluid motion.

To my mind sin wasn't supposed to be so sleek. Sin was supposed to look bloated and milky white with disease. But even at forty, Dickie Vreeman could have been what people think Adam was.

I was summer help for Ed that year. When I think of it now I suppose I could have put everything Dickie ever said to me on one side of a cassette. A friend of mine told me how he once rode five hundred miles with two Navajo men in a van and neither of them talked for more than ten minutes total. Dickie would have liked that style.

Ed's crew had a job downtown that summer when the church finally kicked Dickie out. The man who owned the filling station downtown (business started out as a blacksmith shop years ago; some people said it was the first building in town) wanted to turn the place into a comprehensive car-care facility, couple full stalls for the mechanics, and a chute for an automatic car wash—just drive up, shift the car into neutral, and a set of steel blocks laid into a track in the floor would pull you through, while huge overhead mops slapped up and over the hood, then lifted themselves up the slope of the windshield and roof and flopped down again, as if it could read the lines of the car. All of that was the plan. Owner said he had to change with the times; more people were concerned about how their cars looked than what was going on beneath the hood, he said.

Ed's crew laid the blocks and the brick up front, and Dickie, already ten years of masonry behind him, laid whole walls by himself. When he was on the roof, I hoisted up the buckets full of bricks or wet cement on the block

294

and tackle Ed set on the scaffolding. That was my summer job—three months hand over hand up a rope.

The garage stood in the middle of town, and most every day a dozen retired men in cardigans and windbreakers stood around on the front sidewalks checking progress, especially between nine and ten—the time when most of them stopped in the Wooden Shoe for coffee and picked up the mail a block west at the post office. You really couldn't avoid seeing Dickie, even if you tried, especially since he spent most of July up top. He had a way of intimidating people, even me. When I worked in the back I took off my shirt, but every day there was sun Dickie was down to skin shortly after ten. He could make men really uncomfortable because you could see the definition in his stomach muscles, as if his rib cage kept running down to his waist. He may well have been the only forty-year-old man in town without a belly. Other men thought they themselves looked more like sin than he did. I know.

It wasn't only the fact that he worked so hard that made people sympathize with Dickie. Back in the sixties, fresh out of reformatory, he found a woman (most people said he found her in a bar in Collinsville) and married her after a few months. Four years of marriage wars and she pulled out just like his own mother had done, left him all alone with two kids. That's when he moved back to his own hometown and bought a ramshackle place on the road going north out of town—one of the old houses built Dutch-style, tucked up close to the front sidewalk, as if the village were a city with no room to grow. When you live in houses like that you can hear people talking when they walk by out front, and your windows are open season. Maybe you live in a fishbowl in a place like that, but then everybody does.

But he worked the place like a trooper. He'd get off work around five and just start right in that shack. He built a new peak and left the old square false front up until he was finished. People just about died when he ripped off the old siding and showed the whole village the front he had been nailing up inside for a year. In just one day he did it. The whole place was transformed.

Everybody sympathized with Dickie Vreeman, because he'd come back to town to live with his two kids, even thought he was still a black sheep. He'd done time for assault and battery and some other things years ago, but it took some hair to came back and live in Easton with the very people he'd wronged. And then, of course, that woman had left him with two kids. It wasn't that people didn't want to like him.

Not his uncle Ed either. Ed gave him a job right away, because Ed was a quiet man with principles, the only man I ever worked for that didn't swear. But the two of them were on this collision course, and I could see it coming all summer. It didn't bother Dickie, because Dickie didn't bother much with the church. That was Dickie's only problem—he just didn't go to church. He refused.

Sometime during that previous winter, he met this woman named Penny. She was at least ten years younger than he was, but they had so much in common otherwise: both of them got left behind, except Penny had three kids and she was a woman. She married a bum who used to race his Chev through town; whenever he'd floor it, the thing would sound like it was blowing air. He left her, and Penny moved into a little house a block west from the bank, a block south from Dickie's fine remodeling job. The man she married, named Gimp, moved to Collinsville, and for a long time nobody in Easton heard from him.

Now you can speculate all you want on the way things went with Dickie and Penny, and you know half the folks in town did. I suppose in this new age, Penny and Dickie figured they had all the reason in the world to be sleeping together. Neither of them cared at all about the church or the morals of all those folks who watched them. And one morning early, really early, I saw them standing out on a street halfway between their houses, on the corner of the open lot where a couple of years ago Hartman's lined up their used cars. It was still the pinkish side of morning, but there they were holding hands like some lovelorn teenagers, all cow-eyed and glowing like the sky out east, as if they couldn't stand the thought of having to separate, even for half a day. Neither of them were kids anymore. Both of them had seen a lot.

Penny walked in a way that forced you to watch her. Three kids widened her hips some, and she never wore shorts at all, even though she had long legs; but she had a strong woman's chest that she carried high when she walked. She had the carriage of fallen royalty maybe, shoulders back, eyes running up and down the street as if to see who might be seeing her, partly proud and partly humble, as if she was afraid that someone would think she wasn't as strong as any woman in town. Most men couldn't help looking at her.

Dickie fell in love. Seems odd to say it, because both of them were already battle-scarred and there was at least a decade between them. But they fell in love. People guessed why they wouldn't get married: Penny would lose her ADC and child support and Dickie would have five kids with only the pay from his uncle Ed's masonry crew. Their kids played together like brothers and sisters anyway. Nobody really believed the two of them weren't sleeping together, but people did wonder how on earth they explained it to their kids.

Penny never came around the garage while we worked there, never came to see him up there, but everybody knew they were close—it wasn't something they wanted advertised, even though they weren't kids.

I didn't know when it was coming down, but I knew it was coming. My own father had worked with Dickie Vreeman for years, so I knew it had been a decade or more since he'd been in the church. To me, excommunication seemed like putting the mark of the beast on a person. But I'd been through catechism, and I knew that the church said that discipline was one of what they called the "keys of the kingdom": "whatsoever shall be bound on earth shall be bound in heaven, and whatsoever shall be loosed on earth shall be loosed in heaven." That was the principle. Discipline, people said, was one of the marks of the true church of the Lord.

It wasn't sleeping with Penny that brought it on either. It

was the fact that Dickie never came to communion, maybe not for twenty years. Penny really didn't change the fact that he refused the means of grace, she just tallied another sin of a lesser degree. Excommunication was a matter of principle finally, a matter of the integrity of the church running headlong into the stiffness of Dickie's refusal to come to the Lord's Supper. Even Ed said so.

Early that summer Ed would climb the scaffold and be up there for hours, alone with Dickie. He'd take his trowel along in his back pocket, and it always made the work harder below because they'd be forever at the side looking for more buckets full of wet cement or bricks. He was up there trying to turn his nephew around. But Dickie was all of a grown man already.

Finally Ed would scramble down the scaffolding and look at me. "Can't get that man to wear a hard hat," he told me a couple times. "He flat refuses. All I need is a big fine."

Most noons Dickie would sneak over to Penny's for lunch, and Ed would go home to his wife. But coffee time we'd be together out back where Ed laid a couple rough planks across some blocks.

You could see the way Ed took it all by the way he'd pour coffee from the thermos; the cup would shake just slightly in his fingers, enough so that he was embarrassed. Shaking made him hold the thing in two hands. But we never talked much. None of the Vreemans are talkers. Sometimes Ed would say something about baseball or the weather, but mostly they nodded at each other and looked around as if there was something new to see out back of the restaurant. We'd sit and eat sugar-flecked donuts Ed bought fresh from the bakery.

Only one morning the whole church business came up. Ed's hard hat leaned up toward the back of his head so the strip of hair down his forehead stuck out from the visor.

"Get some company last night, did you, Dickie?" Ed said.

Dickie nodded. The only way you could tell he was forty was the lines in his face. His cheeks were shallow where the skin drew back from his bones. Tight little lines grew out and away from his eyes like sun rays in a kid's drawing. "Doesn't matter anyway," he said.

"Be easier for everybody if you'd just take your paper up to some other church." Ed shook the drip off the edge of the donut.

"That's the church I was born into. They don't want me anymore, they're going to have to throw me out if they got the guts to do it."

Dickie had such quiet blue eyes. He was so quiet that sometimes I was afraid of him.

Ed started to say something, and then he stopped.

People said in a hundred years of church life there had never been an official excommunication. Eventually people just left the church if they were angry or if they didn't feel like belonging anymore. But it was like a Vreeman to be stubborn about it. There was no way anyone could understand what was going on in his head, because he pushed the church to act, almost as if it were a dare, a test of the will of the righteous.

"That's the church I always been in," he told any of the dozens who tried to work with him, just like he told Ed that morning out back on the job.

Dickie didn't turn up for the service itself, of course. The church was vacant then, so they had in a preacher from somewhere up north, an old man who did everything he could to make it seem as sweet as an excommunication could be. What I remember best is the irony of talking about Dickie Vreeman (the preacher called him Richard because that was his christened name) without Dickie being there to hear it. That morning he was with Penny and the kids. Maybe he wasn't even thinking about finally being thrown out. Maybe he didn't care.

I walked home that Sunday with a neighbor kid, son of a big contractor. "First time that's ever happened that I remember," I said. "I never saw anything like that before in this church." I wondered what a kid no more than twelve thought about throwing somebody out the way we did that morning.

"My old man says there comes a time that you got to

toss out the rotten apples," the kid said.

Dickie came in the next morning at seven and he wore that same flannel shirt he always started with during the early hours, two buttons left, both of them around the stomach. Dime-sized holes were in the T-shirt he wore beneath.

There wasn't a thing written on his face—no joy, no guilt, no sorrow, nothing to explain what it felt like to be the first man kicked out in a century of worship in a village church. He climbed up the scaffolding and stood there at the edge cupping a cigarette, looking down at me, waiting to start things up.

On Tuesday the crew from the car wash manufacturers came in to check specs for the installation. We were done with most of the block and all there was left was the elevation of fancy red brick, plus a little finish work on the roof. Most of the morning Ed spent inside, and since there were no doors or windows, I heard the crew talking about the installation. Ed took some notes on the specs, I remember, because it wasn't often I saw Ed with a pencil in his hand.

He hadn't been up there with Dickie all day on Monday. And Tuesday all day it was the manufacturers downstairs.

"Buy you lunch," he says to me just before noon that day.

Ed was the boss. I figured his wife was shopping.

We went next door and took the little table next to the window to the east. The place was filled with people, mostly men, because the Shoe serves real home cooking at noon.

The waitress brought up two specials, without us ordering at all: hot beef sandwich with green beans and potatoes with gravy.

"I don't think it's right, Ed. What the church did to him isn't right at all," I told him.

"Stinks," he said. That's all.

It took me a week before I realized what was happening. Ed stopped talking to Dickie completely. He'd come around and make himself busy in the front some mornings,

300

or else he'd stand at the back and tell me where he'd been bidding another job. He never told me things like that otherwise, because I was only summer help; but I started to understand why he was doing it. He counted on my telling Dickie what was happening, where we'd be going when the job downtown was over. So I told Dickie. And that's the way it went. Dickie never changed, never said much to me at all, but it wasn't like any Vreeman to talk much.

Coffee time they'd sit there at right angles not ten feet from each other, and they wouldn't say a thing, wouldn't even look at each other. If I'd ask about the car wash, Ed would tell me straight out, like a newspaper account meant for Dickie to read, but he'd only look at me when he'd say it, round-faced, in that soft and gentle way of his. Ed never swore once while I worked for him, and rarely did he raise his voice. It was just work for him; in that way he and Dickie were like brothers.

I was old enough to understand what was going on. Ed didn't like excommunication, but he was a church man, and he lived by principle. One night I sat down to read through that form again, the one the old preacher read in church for Dickie Vreeman. "Beloved Christians," it said, "keep no company with him, to the end that he may be ashamed; yet count him not as an enemy, but at times admonish him as you would a brother." Maybe I hadn't heard it that day in church because I was thinking about what Dickie might be doing at the very time the church was throwing him out.

Ed took it all very seriously. It was an awkward silence he kept with his own nephew, signing his checks but otherwise staying out of Dickie's life as if it were charmed with sin itself. All through the end of the July heat, Ed stayed cold as lakeshore spring. And Dickie never—not once—showed the slightest emotion. He just worked all the harder.

One day Penny's ex showed up around back, looking for Dickie.

"Vreeman up there?" he asked me.

"Which one?"

"Dickie-boy?"

I could tell he had been drinking. "You bet," I said.

The wind was strong and from the west, and the man's hair flew in a mess over his eyes and face.

"What time you guys take coffee?" he said.

I told him 3:15.

I knew Dickie must have seen the guy show up, because he was finished up on the roof. He wasn't surprised when I told him the guy had asked about coffee time.

Dickie's bush hair was bleached to a silvery pine color, and his back was brown like dark oak stain. He snapped off his headband when he jumped from the scaffold, and he rung the moisture out with his fist, every single muscle and vein popping in his arm. Gray sweat ran through his fingers and flew off when he flicked his wrist.

"What did he want?" he said.

I told him I didn't know.

Ed got us some long johns that afternoon, but nobody said a thing when Penny's ex showed up again. He had been to the corner during the hour or so he'd been away, and he came back smelling like a keg. The man was tall and gaunt and walked with a stoop, so that when he talked to you, he squinted through the tops of his eyes. People called him Gimp because of the way his shoulders turned in a sort of semicircle. He had a way of moving his head with his whole upper body, as if everything was connected from his waist up. The sleeves of his sweatshirt were cut off halfway up his biceps.

"I got you a proposition, Dickie," he said, "better than the one you're giving Penny and the kids."

Ed got up right away and hiked up the scaffolds to the roof. I knew he didn't want to hear any of it. I didn't know where to go right away.

"I know what you been doing to my ex, see?" Gimp said. "I got proof—even photographs—'cause I hired this private eye, and he knows all your comings in and your goings forth."

Dickie never showed emotion. His eyes were blue and soft, but he never once looked down.

"Look man, I'm strapped. I can't make them payments

for the rest of my life. She's taken me down the river, see? Shoot, I got my own life too, you know, and everything I get I got to pay in for them kids."

"You got my pity," Dickie said.

"Look, it ain't one bit fair that you're getting her and not paying for it. I don't call that justice, Dickie." He crossed his arms on his chest and his muscles, long and thin, flattened over his fingers.

"No business of yours," Dickie said. "You got no right at all to be watching over me or her."

"Listen, man to man, let's talk. I got nothing against what you're getting off her—she wants a man like you, then that's fine with me. But I'm saying it ain't fair and I got the law on my side too, see?"

I shoved the rest of the long john into my mouth and wandered back over to the trough to slosh up the mix and keep it soft.

"I think it'd be in your own best interest to get lost," Dickie said.

"It's nothing against you personally, Dickie. I just want out of the payments, and it doesn't seem right to me that you're fooling around and not taking a dime's worth of responsibility." Gimp pulled the hair back out of his eyes.

Dickie looked around for a minute to see if anybody else was around back.

"All I'm saying is let me go of them payments, see? I could care less if you marry that woman. I just want out."

"You got nothing to say, Gimp." Dickie raised both arms up over his head and flicked on the sweatband.

"To heck, I don't! I can get me a court order that keeps you out of that house forever. I got the goods on you, Dickie. You know what you are? You're an impediment to the moral upbringing of my own sweet children." You could feel the cut in his straight-edge laugh. "I can keep you right out of her bed from this time forth."

Dickie cleared his nose with one finger against a nostril.

Gimp stood there straight, arms crossed. "You're crazy if you think you can mess around free. I got the law, man. You ain't got nothin'."

"Get out of here," Dickie said.

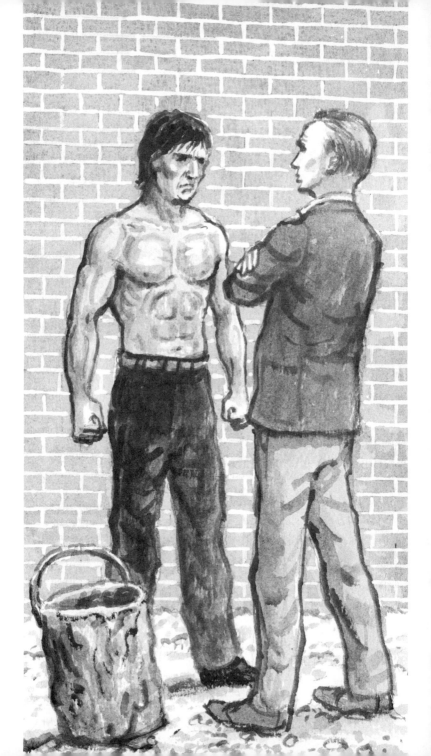

"You get her to stop soaking me and you can have her—it's just that simple. Otherwise, so help me, I'll shut you off tight and put you back in jail."

There was nothing on Dickie's face but one twitching eye. He raised up his hands on his waist and turned them backwards so his thumbs pointed out at Gimp.

"Ain't nothing but a matter of money, that's all. Shoot, old man like yourself—"

For a minute they stood there staring, then Gimp backed off slowly, maybe ten steps, until he turned and walked away, his head ducking forward the way a pigeon walks. Then he stopped and half-turned. "Dickie," he said, "you ought to know what it's like to go without, you old jailbird."

When I looked at Dickie, he wasn't breathing. In the sun, the sweat lit up like glitter where it streamed from his hair down his neck. He waited until Gimp got to the corner of the east wall before he took off after him. The sound that came out from his chest was something of a growl and something of a scream.

Gimp heard Dickie take off, and he split without looking back. I knew right then there was going to be a beating, and I knew right off that Dickie could kill the man. In a second I knew all of it. In that little time I thought of Dickie back in jail.

And just like that this five-gallon pail full of wet cement dropped from the roof like a sledge. It cracked the old concrete where it hit not a two full strides in front of Dickie. The bottom edge of the pail crushed from the impact, so it stood there, right-side-up, crooked as some comedian's hat.

Gimp never knew what happened, but Dickie stopped cold in his tracks, his hands out front of him like a surgeon's. Then he looked up and saw his Uncle Ed at the edge of the roof with his hands on his hips.

Dickie picked up the pail and held it high over his head. The cement flew out in thick globs. Then he flung the empty bucket against the block wall, picked it up and hurled it again and again until the thing was bent up like a soup can.

And Ed stood there up above in very principled silence. "Don't know how many times I'm going to have to tell that boy to wear a hat," he said, looking at me.